G000153673

POCKET
INFORMATION
TECHNOLOGY

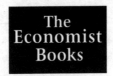

The
Economist
Books

POCKET

INFORMATION
TECHNOLOGY

JOHN BROWNING

THE ECONOMIST IN ASSOCIATION WITH
PROFILE BOOKS LTD

Profile Books Ltd
58A Hatton Garden, London EC1N 8LX

Published by Profile Books Ltd
in association with
The Economist Newspaper Ltd

Printed by
LEGO S.p.a. - Vicenza - Italy

A CIP catalogue record for this book is available
from the British Library

ISBN 1 86197 032 3

Contents

INTRODUCTION

Pocket Information Technology is one of a series of management titles that is designed to bring clarity to specialist subjects. It is written by John Browning, who was formerly a business, economics and technology correspondent with *The Economist*. He is now European Editor of *Wired* and a writer and consultant specialising in information technology. The book is divided into three parts.

Part 1 comprises essays on how companies are having to re-engineer themselves, the information economy, the growth of electronic commerce, and the threats to Microsoft's powerful position in the computer industry.

Part 2 is an A–Z of terms, acronyms and jargon such as Ada and Archie, MUD and MOO, Vapourware and Zeroth. In this section words in small capitals usually indicate a separate entry; however, all acronyms such as EU and TV are in small caps even if they have no separate entry.

Part 3 consists of several appendixes, including the world's largest IT suppliers, the growth in computers connected to the Internet, and a list of abbreviations and acronyms that appear in the book.

Other titles in the series are:

Pocket Accounting
Pocket Director
Pocket Employer
Pocket Finance
Pocket Investor
Pocket Law
Pocket Manager
Pocket Marketing
Pocket MBA
Pocket Negotiator
Pocket Strategy
Pocket Telecommunications

Part 1
ESSAYS

RE-INVENTING RE-ENGINEERING

"And now for something completely different." Monty Python's catchphrase is being adopted by companies around the world. Executives everywhere have seized upon the idea that technology can set them free from all the old rules and constraints of management. They have not yet entirely figured out what the new rules might be. But that has not stopped them from using technology to change everything anyway. Originally, this ongoing managerial revolution marched under the banner of re-engineering. But like most catchphrases popular among marketing people and management consultants, it was abused until it became meaningless. Today's buzzword is intranets. Call it what you will the impact of technology is the same: a new set of rules to compete by.

Michael Hammer published re-engineering's manifesto in 1990 in the *Harvard Business Review* in an article entitled "Don't Automate, Obliterate". In the following years nearly every big company, and most small ones, embarked on at least one re-engineering project. By most estimates, about half of these efforts failed to reach their goals. Obliterating is harder than it sounds.

The initial success rate for intranets is higher, mainly because the initial goals are typically narrower. Most companies install intranets to reduce network-administration charges and to improve internal communication – and, according to a study by Meta Consulting, released in 1997, most do. But having done this, managers once again find themselves face to face with an uncharted future. Because intranets use the same technology as the Internet, they enable a company to communicate as easily with those outside the company (suppliers and customers) as those within. So managers can redraw the boundaries of the corporation – if only they can figure out how.

Many executives will want to imitate Mervyn's, a middle-sized, middle-market chain of about 300 department stores spread across the USA. It added tens of millions of dollars per year to profits after spending nine months re-engineering its inventory-control systems. By using computers to track sales more closely and to respond more quickly, it managed to reduce inventory dramatically and to halve the frequency with which goods are out of stock when a customer asks for them. Or Chrysler, which by 1997 had put over 30,000 copies of Netscape's Web browser on its employee's desktops to enable them to share information more easily. Or Aetna Insurance, which uses push media to keep roving salesmen up-to-date with product developments and company news.

These companies are not alone. Banks, carmakers, insurance companies, retailers and a host of others can boast inspiringly successful tales of using computers to change the way they work. But there is still a long way to go. Despite the billions spent putting computers on managers' desktops, growth in the overall productivity of the white-collar workers who use the machines has only recently begun to reflect the investment. Underlying every attempt to change companies to take advantage of computers and networks is the larger process of competitive markets groping towards a new equilibrium; an equilibrium that is suited to economies dominated by trading in ideas rather than things and powered by computers rather than motors.

Work harder, faster

Two factors guide technology-driven change. First, as most executives have already realised, computers and networks enable work to be done radically differently from how it was done before. Second, as they are now coming to realise, information, the raw material of today's service economies, is a different commodity, with different properties, from the iron and coal that fuelled the industrial revolution. These two factors rock the very foundations of industrial organisation.

One of the simplest and most profound consequences of the new realities of capitalism is a shift from sequential processes to simultaneous ones.

Information on a computer can be copied instantly and costlessly, so many people can work on the same thing at once, instead of passing it, step by time-consuming step, from one to another. This simple realisation is the source of some of the most impressive savings of re-engineering. IBM Credit, for example, used this insight to reduce the time needed to approve financial terms for the purchase of big computers – and thus to close the deal – from over a week to under four hours. Insurance companies have cut claims-processing times from weeks to minutes. But the new ways of working are not just faster, they are also fundamentally different.

The technology that breaks down the barriers inhibiting people from different parts of the company from working on the same job at the same time also breaks down barriers that separate companies from their customers. One of the first waves of disintermediation – that is, of removing the middlemen between buyers and sellers – came in the 1970s, when people began to get their cash direct from a hole in the wall rather than from a teller. Then car-makers began placing orders directly into their suppliers' production-planning computers rather than picking from a warehouse, and Wal-Mart began stocking its shelves with Procter & Gamble goods directly from P&G's inventory, managed by P&G's computers, instead of via its own warehouses.

Intranets bring further disintermediation. Companies that distribute goods over the Internet – like the Internet Shopping Network, which in 1994 was purchased by television's Home Shopping Network – have two big advantages over conventional mail-order. They need neither to print catalogues, because would-be customers browse their databases electronically, nor to employ banks of people to answer telephones, because customers place orders directly into the computers that fill them. Soon such disintermediation could affect everybody who makes their living by answering a telephone, from stockbrokers to warehouse staff.

But disintermediation is not the only impact of computer networks. As intranets grow into extranets encompassing suppliers and customers, they also enable alliances of small firms to take on jobs of a scale previously manageable only by giants. The result of these pressures is to break down all of the old corporate certainties.

On the front line

Technology creates not just an opportunity for a transformation of work, but also the necessity to do so. Sharing information in databases makes it easier for everybody to see the big picture of the customer's problems, and thus to do the right thing rather than simply to follow the job description. But, as Tom Malone of the Massachusetts Institute of Technology (MIT) pointed out in an article entitled "Electronic Markets and Electronic Hierarchies", published in the *Communications of the Association for Computing Machinery*, it also creates a managerial paradox.

At the simplest level, information technology makes it easier for firms to gather more information. To put that information to use, however, managers will want to use it to make decisions, which means turning more employees into decision-makers. And therein lies the rub. Traditional management involves telling people what to do. Yet the whole point of decision-makers is that they should decide for themselves what to do. Thus to persevere with a traditional managerial line of command is to waste most of the potential of new technology. But to eschew it is to step resolutely into a brave new managerial world.

Small, in the new world, is beautiful. Information work usually leads to diseconomies of scale. Although big factories may produce goods more cheaply than small ones, big committees often produce worse decisions, more expensively than small ones. Fred Brooks chronicled the phenomenon in his book *The Mythical Man Month*, an account of a huge, and hugely over-budget, software project undertaken at IBM in the late 1960s. Dr Brooks, who was managing the project, was shocked to find that adding more staff simply made the project fall further behind and become more expensive. The problem, he deduced, was that the extra time needed to co-ordinate a larger group of workers – to keep everybody up to speed on the underlying knowledge they needed to work together – quickly overwhelmed the extra contribution they could make to the project.

Although it is hard to assign cause and effect for changes that can be observed only through broad-brush statistics, similar forces could be reshaping the economy as a whole. In the USA, the UK and Germany the average size of firms began to fall in the early 1970s after nearly 200 years of steady growth. Erik Brynjolfsson of MIT further found that, industry sector by industry sector, declines in firm size were strongly correlated to investment in information technology. Even big firms are breaking down large bureaucracies in favour of smaller, often self-managing, teams.

To function at the pace of today's highest-performing companies, managers must become coaches rather than commanders; they must set the context in which others make decisions rather than specifying the exact content of those decisions. There is simply no time to tell people what to do, or to check and cross-check work as it moves through a bureaucratic hierarchy. Instead, managers must increasingly focus on giving employees the background knowledge, the information and the resources to make decisions for themselves, preferably the right ones. This is, of course, easier said than done. It is one thing to recognise intellectually that real authority lies in the number of people who respect your ideas; it is another entirely to give up direct command over your department in the hope of leading by example and inspiration alone.

Golden rules

Given the scale of the changes that technology brings, it is no wonder that learning the new rules of management is still a struggle. Nonetheless, three lessons have emerged which can help today's managers at least to struggle more productively than their predecessors.

1 Focus on results. By definition, re-engineering involves creating new ways of doing things. A crucial aid in that process of innovation is to focus on what needs to be done rather than the existing procedures for doing it; on creating demand rather than marketing; or on delivering goods on time rather than order-taking and inventory management. Focusing on results helps innovators to realise that some parts of their old procedures are no longer necessary, and that they can simplify dramatically.

2 Build technology infrastructure. The technology that drives corporate change can also hinder it. Change in many firms is stymied by systems which, by automating specific business procedures, have effectively cast them in electronic concrete. A better way, many companies find, is to try from the beginning to separate the generic functions that technology provides – like communications and databases – from the specific business logic of a given procedure. With intranets to speed communication both within the firm and outside, and data warehouses to pool data from a variety of sources for a variety of uses, change can happen as fast as people can make it – not merely as fast as the machines will allow it.

3 Start as you would finish. One of biggest and yet most understandable mistakes, which many re-engineering projects make, is to try to define carefully where they will end up before they begin. Re-engineering often creates such dramatic changes that it is impossible to imagine the details of work in the new world when the company sets forth from the old. Companies that try to project ahead too carefully often end up with five-year plans which are irrelevant by the time they approach completion; and, worse, they create top-heavy planning bureaucracies in doing so. Mervyn's, by contrast, based its successful re-engineering of inventory management on a prototype which took two months to build, and another two months to prove its business value. Its basic value established, the system was improved steadily as it was rolled out, with suggestions based on use of the technology rather than theoretical hopes.

4 Bring your customers inside. Web sites are not just a cheap way of achieving broader distribution; they also allow companies to form closer relationships with customers. A classic example is FedEx, which has linked its logistics systems to its Web site, *www.fedex.com*. By allowing customers to track their own packages, it both improves service and saves money on handling telephone enquiries. Cisco, a leading manufacturer of network equipment, sells hundreds of millions of dollars worth of its products from its Web site. More importantly, it also does most of its customer support there, giving customers better answers to their questions, faster.

Despite the fact that nobody really knows what they are doing with new media and new technology – and all of the frustration, the failures and the confusion that this entails – there is ample reason for soaring optimism. For the best is probably still to come. As Paul David, an economic historian at Stanford University, has pointed out, industry often takes much longer than expected to pick up new ways of working. At the end of the 19th century the advance of electricity made possible dramatically more productive factories, with individual motors at each workbench rather than a single, giant steam engine linked to workbenches by belts and pulleys. Proponents of the technology began proclaiming its virtues in about 1900, yet big productivity gains did not appear until the 1920s. So, as personal computers started becoming popular in the mid-1980s, the first decade of the 21st century could be a very good time indeed.

THE INFORMATION ECONOMY

By 1997 the global Internet had outstripped the population of most European countries. As it grew, the Internet inevitably became both a potentially powerful force for changing the world and a huge potential market. As that realisation spread, the issues that dominate debate over the Net changed. Instead of worrying about how to grow the network, politicians, businessmen and consumers increasingly found themselves arguing about how to govern it.

As befits the wealthy suburb of global media that the Internet is, the debate over governance keeps returning to two issues: sex and shopping. Translated into the language and technology of the Internet, both these issues revolve around questions which most politicians never thought they would have to master, such as encryption, filtering software and intellectual property. To regulate the Internet, legislatures must not only learn about new technology, but also challenge old assumptions about how media works. The first question to answer is just what sort of thing the Internet might be.

In his book *Technologies of Freedom*, Ithiel de Sola Pool, a professor of communications, pointed out that the world's media have evolved three quite different regulatory regimes. In the world of print, governments by and large defend the rights of the owners of printing presses to say whatever they want, as long as they are also willing to defend their words against any charges of libel they may attract. In broadcast, governments restrict what can be transmitted on the (today largely spurious) ground that a scarce resource like radio spectrum must be used for the good of the whole community. In communications, governments merely require that telecoms companies and the post office provide equal service to whoever wants to send messages through their networks; beyond that, the carrier bears no responsibility.

The Internet contains elements of all three systems. It enables person-to-person communication via e-mail. It hosts thousands upon thousands of electronic publications and Web sites. Some of these Web sites already contain video to rival the images on television; as bandwidth rises, more video should become available. So which set of rules should apply?

Who rules the Net?

Predictably, governments kicked off the debate by trying to apply the most restrictive set of regulations available: those for broadcast. The German government prosecuted Compuserve, among others, for providing access to *alt.sex* and other USENET news groups which are allegedly obscene under German law. In 1996 the US Congress passed the Communications Decency Act, which would have made it a crime to put potentially offensive material on the Internet where it might be encountered by a child. Given that children seem to pop up just about everywhere on the Net – from academic Web sites to highly classified NASA computers – the law was promptly ruled an unconstitutional violation of free speech.

As the debate goes on, though, politicians are discovering that the Internet is not just television with a mouse attached. It is not even a single thing. Making sensible decisions about regulating pornography – or indeed any aspect of the Net – requires some distinctions that governments have only dimly begun to grasp.

Content versus conduit. Compuserve Germany, like other Internet service providers (ISP), argues that it is ridiculous to hold it responsible for the messages it carries. It simply transmits packets of data, without knowing or caring what they mean. Neither post offices nor phone companies are asked to snoop on or censor the messages they carry, for good reason. So why should an ISP?
Interactive versus broadcast. Everybody on the Internet effectively owns a printing press and video transmitter. So restrictions on publications quickly become indistinguishable from restraints

on free speech. Moreover, given the vast bandwidth of the Internet, technology has made irrelevant old arguments from the traditional world of broadcasting: that the scarcity of bandwidth justifies controlling content to ensure that its use serves the greatest good of the greatest number. There is capacity for everybody to say anything to anybody.

Public versus private. The Internet blurs the once clear distinctions between public speech, published for a wide audience, and a private conversation between two people. Most Web sites are clearly public and most e-mail exchanges clearly private. But in between lies a whole new range of mailing lists, bulletin boards and other semi-private communications. Most Web sites with adult material now go to some lengths to exclude children. But there is no legal or social consensus over what, exactly, is private.

Pull versus push. Because of the Internet's global, distributed structure it is both practically and legally almost impossible to stop someone putting material on to the Internet. So the traditional approach to censorship – thou shalt not publish – does not work. What does work is software that prevents people from accessing material from the Internet. Filtering software using the PICS standard, for example, allows anybody to rate any Web site on any criteria – and set Web browsers to block automatically access to those Web sites whose criteria do not fall within approved bounds. Here too, though, there is no consensus over who should use the software and on what terms. Should librarians, for example, be required to use filtering software to exclude pornography from computers in public libraries? Should they even be allowed to?

Free speech and free trade. Because the Internet is both a communications medium and the delivery network for a global trade in ideas, issues of free speech rapidly become tangled up in issues of free trade. Singapore, for example, routes most Internet communications through government-owned computers and blocks packets from sites it disapproves of, typically because they show too much flesh or say too many nasty things about the Singapore government. It says economics and business have nothing to do with its decisions, but that does not eliminate the economic impact on the publishers. Is this fair trade? Would it be fair if the French succeeded in getting the EU to guarantee minimum local content for both television and the Web in order to protect European culture from the American variety?

None of these distinctions is easy, and they are not the only tough choices governments face about the Internet. Another vexed set of questions concerns how much control individuals should be given over their own private communications.

Nowhere to hide

An irony of the Net-censorship debate is that, even as governments try to push sex out of sight, most are also battling to keep other communications from becoming too secret. Public-key encryption creates codes even governments cannot break. So the American government is leading a global effort to stop people from using it.

Led by the USA's National Security Agency, security agencies say that they need the ability to wiretap in order to catch criminals and terrorists. In 1994 the US government passed the Digital Telephony Act, which required makers of digital switches to modify their technology to make it more wiretap friendly. Since then it has doggedly argued for restraints on the use of encryption. First, it has classified public-key encryption technology as a weapon and banned the export of all but the least powerful varieties. More importantly, it has also lobbied for "key escrow" schemes, which would require users of encryption to deposit copies of their keys with government-licensed agencies, which, in turn, would be required to hand them over to security agencies on demand.

Such schemes have met with heated opposition. Most of the arguments centre on civil liberties, for the good reason that the proposals make a huge dent in individual rights to privacy. It is one thing to create search warrants to enable law-enforcement agencies to search for evidence of a crime; indeed, the obvious extension of search warrants to cyberspace – decryption warrants that would require individuals to decrypt messages or face contempt of court – are an alternative to key escrow favoured by many civil libertarians. But it is another, more intrusive thing to require, say, locksmiths to hold a copy of the keys and combinations to every lock they install so that security agencies can search surreptitiously, without inconvenience. Yet this is effectively what key escrow schemes would do.

The more subtle problem with key escrow schemes is that they create economic insecurity, undermining the ability of the Internet to serve as a conduit for electronic commerce. As politicians are only slowly beginning to realise, the technology of public-key encryption links secrecy and identity in new and subtle ways. The technology that encrypts messages is also that which creates the digital signatures that establish legal responsibility and binding contracts. Measures which make it easier to eavesdrop also increase the risks of forgery, or even of digital economic terrorism.

For all of these reasons a committee of computer scientists and academics – including Ron Rivest and Whit Diffie, two of the inventors of public-key encryption – issued a report in May 1997 which pointed out that the US government's key escrow proposals would create both unnecessary risk and expense. In response, the government proposed yet another encryption bill, which would require key escrow.

You own your own words

Reluctant though it may be to allow individuals control over the privacy of their data, the US government does want to give companies greater ownership rights over the information they put on the Web. Updating copyright for the digital age was the subject of a meeting of the World Intellectual Property Organisation (WIPO) in Geneva in December 1996. At the conference the Americans argued for two crucial extensions to copyright for the digital age. One would have extended copyright to cover the transient copies of a work made in transmitting material over the Internet or in browsing it on a screen. The other would have given creators of databases some ownership rights over the facts they collect. Although backed by the Europeans, the Americans lost on both issues.

The database treaty was hardest fought. Many European countries already give database-builders some ownership rights. In the USA, by contrast, it is quite legal for a would-be supplier of telephone directories to copy entries out of a rival's directories (a Supreme Court decision, *Feist v Rural Telephone*, defends the right to do so). Although it was the Americans who proposed the adoption of European database protections, the proposals were killed in large part by lobbying from US organisations. Academics feared that the new regulations might deny them access to research results. Broadcasters feared that they might have to start paying hefty fees for sports statistics. Developing countries feared that the flow of educational material from the developed world might be hindered.

Proposals to extend copyright to transient copies were similarly quashed. Computer and Internet companies feared that these legal restrictions could cut deeply into Web browsing. Hollywood, meanwhile, wanted them for precisely that reason: to ensure that viewing video or text on a computer screen was legally equivalent to seeing it in a cinema.

Such arguments will run and run. But, despite all the lobbying and brouhaha, resolution of these issues is likely to be a slow process. Cyberspace is a vast place, and the dilemmas it poses are unfamiliar. Sound government for it can only follow a complete exploration of the new vistas and possibilities that it opens up. And that process has only just begun.

LET'S MAKE AN E-DEAL

Electronic commerce offers some overwhelming advantages over conventional shopping. It is cheaper. Electronic shops do not need expensive high-street real estate and they carry even less inventory than many mail-order shops. And, in theory, it is more convenient. Shoppers can hunt for bargains around the world without leaving home. These advantages will not run existing shops out of business. People will never stop pinching the peaches or trying on clothes, and much shopping is done as much for the pleasure of the experience as to actually bring home the goods. But the inevitable rise of electronic commerce will nonetheless change the face of business forever.

Challenges

Electronic commerce presents companies with two related challenges. The first, and most pressing, is to understand the sources of competitive advantage in the electronic realm. For all of the new digital abilities that might inspire customers to switch their purchases from shop to Web site also make it easy for them to switch from one Web site to another. Second, how can companies use their new electronic capabilities to improve their real-world offerings? Although it is early days yet, some answers are beginning to evolve.

In 1996 American consumers spent about $500m online. Although predicting future growth is tricky, estimates for the year 2000 range from $6 billion all the way up to $16 billion. Personal finance, entertainment (including books and CDs), travel and computer equipment are expected to lead this retail growth. Business-to-business sales already far outstrip retail sales. In 1997 GE and Cisco expected to achieve sales of over $1 billion each via the Web, and Dell Computer expected to clock up sales of well over $500m. Companies are discovering that doing business electronically brings big changes in their relationships with customers and suppliers alike.

How it's working

To see how, look at some examples of successful online experiments.

- Amazon.com touts itself as "the world's largest bookstore" with over 1m titles available. Yet it does not have a physical store. Nor does it hold more than a few hundred of the best-selling titles in its warehouse. Instead it has an extensive catalogue of books in print at its Web site (*www.amazon.com*) and electronic links to the warehouses of book publishers and distributors, so that it can ship direct to customers from there. Better, it vastly extends its virtual shelf space through an "associates" program, which enables anyone running a Web site that mentions books to create a hyperlink back to Amazon.com, to enable them to buy the book online.
- CDNow, as the name suggests, sells CDs online at *www.cdnow.com*. It can, and does, compete on price with high-street music shops. But its lasting advantage comes from the way in which it is reinventing the experience of buying music. It links CD titles in its catalogue to online reviews. It lists the influences on each artist and it also lists artists who were in turn influenced by that artist, so that someone who likes, say, Aretha Franklin, can easily find more music of a similar kind. By giving music-buyers more information, CDNow is gradually making shopping online not just cheaper but better.
- OnSale is an online auction house focusing on cheapness. It sells mostly electronic equipment at *www.onsale.com*, much of it the surplus inventory of more conventional stores. But instead of trying to set fire-sale prices, it uses the interactive capabilities of the Internet to hold online auctions, and so continually finds the best price the market will bear.

- Auto-by-Tel sells cars on the Internet at *www.autobytel.com*. Its market is individuals who know what they want, but would prefer to save the time spent roaming from dealer to dealer haggling over prices. It also saves dealers the time spent haggling with customers who end up buying elsewhere. It asks buyers to put in firm bids for cars and then searches its network for a dealer willing to meet the price.
- E*Trade trades US company shares without stockbrokers at *www.etrade.com*. Instead of clients calling a broker, who then taps the order into a keyboard, clients simply type in their own orders. Needless to say, E*Trade offers savings on commissions. One of E*Trade's British counterparts, Electronic Share Information, has even higher ambitions. By reducing the cost of issuing and trading equity, it hopes to create a new market that can provide finance for small and medium-sized companies now reliant on banks and venture capitalists.
- Firefly.com is trying to turn the notion of brand on its head. Many advertising campaigns have tried to sell products on the ground that people you like like the product. Firefly turns this theory to practice. It asks members of its group to rate the products and services they find online. Their tastes are matched, and the information is used to answer two questions. First, would somebody like you like a particular product under evaluation? Second, when you are looking for recommendations in a field you know nothing about, what do people like you like? This is market research made live.

New commercial world

All these experiments take advantage of the ubiquity and interactivity of the new media to weave information ever more closely into commerce. Instead of creating advertisements that recommend a company to a potential buyer, online advertisements introduce them to each other. The relationship can be taken further online. The customer can ask questions, or maybe even buy the company's goods then and there. Peering further into the future, it is likely that as well as moving shopping online, online information will also move into the shops.

Universal resource locators (URL) are popping up in all sorts of places. United Parcel Service trucks carry the sign *www.ups.com* to signal to potential customers that, like FedEx, the company enables them to track parcels online. Advertisements painted on the side of London taxi-cabs carry a URL to show the curious where to find more information than they can read in moving traffic. So do products ranging from soft drinks to records. Supermarkets, meanwhile, are experimenting with wireless technology that can beam product information from transmitters in the shelves to a screen in the shopping trolley. Forget a recipe while shopping and you could just look it up on the Net as you cruise the aisles.

Although the details are far from clear, building new shopping habits and experiences will provide the answers to the problem of maintaining customer loyalty online. In a new and unfamiliar world, companies that can persuade customers to spend their time and mental energy to learn new ways of doing things can create habits that build fortunes. The learning starts – here for both companies and customers.

Leaders of the Pack

Some companies achieve greatness; others have greatness thrust upon them. Each in its own era, both IBM and Microsoft have managed both. For in the computer industry, success breeds success. The popularity of technologies developed by IBM and Microsoft increased their power to set future technological standards, and so set the course of competition in a direction which favoured their own products. Although both firms have been extensively investigated by the USA's Justice Department for allegedly anti-competitive practices, no serious charges were brought against either. Given the industry's history, two questions dominate discussions of the future of computer markets. Who, if anyone, will next wield the sorts of powers held by IBM and Microsoft? Or, in a maturing computer market, will this sort of power become as obsolete as the vacuum tube?

Elements of success

Although IBM and Microsoft came to prominence in different eras and with different technologies, many basic elements of their success stories are the same. In 1965 IBM shipped the first of its System 360 range of mainframe computers. Not only was the 360 based on the then new technology of integrated circuits, but it was also the first family of computers to offer companies a chance to upgrade from small entry-level machines to more powerful ones, as their computing needs grew, without changing their software.

Microsoft got its chance to shine in 1981, when its DOS operating system was offered by IBM on its first personal computer. Unusually for IBM, in its haste to get a personal computer to market, it did not acquire exclusive rights to either DOS or the Intel microprocessor which powered its computer. Yet with the reassuring bulk of IBM behind them, both technologies quickly became *de facto* standards in the market. In the 16 months after the launch of the IBM personal computer, Microsoft licensed DOS to 50 other computer-makers.

For both IBM in 1965 and Microsoft in 1981, an initial lead on the competition launched them into a self-reinforcing cycle of success. Part of that self-reinforcement came from customers' fears. In the fast-moving world of technology, even knowledgeable customers can make expensive mistakes. So, if all else fails, buying the most popular brand means that you are no more embarrassed than most other people. (Or, to put it more succinctly: "Nobody ever got fired for buying IBM.")

But there is a stronger reason for going with the majority: protecting investments made in software. Because IBM and Microsoft held the largest market share, more developers of commercial software created products for their computers than for rivals. The availability of software, in turn, increases the value of the computers it runs on, which helps to inspire more software, and so on. A steady flow of software innovation, in turn, helps to convince companies that data which can only be accessed using some particular kind of software will continue to be accessible via such software.

IBM's fall

IBM fell from grace largely because it underestimated both the personal computer in general and the power of the forces its own personal computer had set in motion. In the USA, at least, sales of personal computers grew at about 22% per year through the 1980s, to about $25 billion in 1994, while sales of mainframes grew at only about 4% per year, to $16 billion. This created a conundrum for IBM. Even today, mainframe computers account for just under half of IBM's revenue, and by far the most profitable part. Mainframe customers require many services, all of which they pay for, and IBM can hold these customers tight within the embrace of its proprietary technical architecture. Yet the mainframe market was stagnating, so throughout the 1980s IBM tried, and failed, to innovate its way back to into the driver's seat in personal computers as well as mainframes.

Part of IBM's problem was that its products were expensive, the legacy of the high corporate overheads developed to provide a handholding service to mainframe customers. But the larger, more subtle problem for IBM was simply that its potential customers did not trust it. They feared that IBM would do what was good for IBM, not for its customers. Competitive personal computer markets, where any number of vendors could buy Intel chips and Microsoft operating systems to build computers compatible with the technical standards set by IBM, offered freedom as well as low prices. IBM tried to woo customers back into its fold with new lines of personal computers, which contained proprietary technologies. Customers resisted. But the final straw came with IBM's break with Microsoft over operating-system strategy.

Although IBM and Microsoft developed OS/2 jointly as the successor to DOS, the two gradually split over strategy. IBM felt its customers wanted the advanced features of OS/2. Microsoft thought that most computer users were not ready and would prefer Windows, which was less technically ambitious but required less computing muscle and technical expertise to run. By 1992 IBM and Microsoft were in competition, and Microsoft won. In that year IBM sold 1m copies of OS/2, while Microsoft sold 10m copies of Windows. As it is the software of operating systems that increasingly determines what computers can and cannot do, this victory has left Microsoft as the company most likely to dictate the direction of the next steps in the personal computer revolution.

The Microsoft challenge
Microsoft's challenge has three parts:

- to continue to dominate the market for desktop operating systems;
- to expand further its healthily growing sales of word processors, spreadsheets and other applications software;
- to move into the new markets being opened up by networks and other new media.

Dominate on...

As strong as Microsoft's position is on the desktop, that position is simply too valuable for Microsoft to remain unchallenged. By 1997, with IBM's OS/2 relegated to the ranks of the technologically quaint, the strongest challenge to Microsoft came from the Network Computer (NC).

The brainchild of Larry Ellison of database-maker Oracle, working with Sun Microsystems and IBM, the NC tries to make computers cheaper to run by splitting them in half. Instead of giving each computer a hard disk on which to store its own copies of programs and data, NCs take both software and data from a central server. The advantage is that centralisation makes the machines much easier to manage, keeping software and data always up to date. For corporations, at least, management makes up the majority of the cost of owning a computer.

Sun, IBM and others reckon that this administrative saving will prove to be the lever that can prise Microsoft off the corporate desktop. They have a point. But in practice, achieving the savings they offer will require both a lot of bandwidth to move programs and data quickly to the desktop, and efficient, responsive central IT management. Homes lack the bandwidth for the NC, and even many corporations fail one or both of these requirements.

...diversify from desktop...

Microsoft is not going to topple soon. But if it wishes to grow, it must succeed in the third challenge diversification from the desktop. Personal computer markets are reaching saturation. There are some fairly easy pickings to be made by adapting Windows for small, handheld devices, But the big opportunity and the big challenge is in expanding on to networks. It is here that Microsoft runs the risk of being hoist with its own competitive petard.

Microsoft's first venture into the online world was the Microsoft Network (MSN). This was originally conceived as an online service that would provide e-mail, electronic chat and an electronic library-cum-shopping-mall. Somewhat as an after-thought to the orginal vision, MSN would also provide links to the larger Internet. Shortly before its launch, however, Bill Gates had a Pauline conversion to the virtues of Internet technology. Instead of a proprietary network, MSN was rapidly converted to an Internet content provider. MSN still offers Internet access, but with little proprietary technology; and, if telecoms companies eventually offer cheaper and better Net access, Mr Gates says that the access business could fade away. The future lies in providing content and services.

So Microsoft is effectively diversifying into media, retail and banking. It hired Michael Kinsley, former editor of *The New Republic*, to create a new online magazine called *Slate* (which, it turns out, reads remarkably like *The New Republic*). It created a series of local guides and listing publications on the Web, called Sidewalk, which gave news and reviews about what is happening in Seattle, New York and other big cities. It launched a Web site to sell travel and another to sell financial services. It entered joint ventures with NBC, to create news and information for both cable television and the Web, and with First Data, the world's largest processor of online payments, to create electronic bill-paying services.

...and try anything new

Microsoft seems determined to have a go at every interesting opportunity that technology throws up, and given its cash balances it can well afford to do so. The big question, though, is whether Microsoft is just another well-heeled competitor, flush with smart and aggressive people, or whether its dominance of desktop software can give it competitive advantage in other areas as well.

Certainly, in technology markets Microsoft seems unable to resist the temptation to try to link new products to established old ones. No sooner did Sun Microsystems launch Java, a language which creates programs that can run on any and all operating systems, than Microsoft began trying to add extensions and new functions to the language that would work only on Windows. It seems likely that Microsoft will similarly try to link innovations in the technology of electronic commerce – new bill-paying systems, for example – to its operating system as well.

But such linkages can reach only so far. Tying Microsoft's media and retail ventures to its operating systems, for example, would tax the business ingenuity even of Microsoft's managers. Successful attempts at linkage annoy Microsoft customers and raise fears that the company is trying to lock them in. Unsuccessful attempts simply enrage them.

In the longer term, the value of Microsoft's proposition is that it enables customers to use more software and services than its competitors. Every time Microsoft cuts out a competitor by linking one of its products to another, it chips away at its own strength. One way or another, this relentless market dynamic promises to chip away at Microsoft's market power just as Microsoft itself eroded IBM's. Microsoft's huge financial strength will enable it to battle powerfully for important markets. Netscape, for example, gives away its browser to win market share, but Microsoft can afford to give away its rival browser for longer and still put more R&D expenditure into it. What Microsoft cannot afford to do, though, is to exclude Netscape altogether by forging a seamless link between its browser and its operating system.

The last leader?

The gradual opening up of markets, as expansion weakens the technical ties between different products, may make Microsoft the last leader of the computer pack. Not because its power will last forever, because it will not. But because after Microsoft a combination of maturity and the new capabilities of networks are likely to make computer markets more diverse. Instead of one dominant leader, many lesser ones may develop.

Given enough computing power and communications bandwidth, it is possible largely to break free of the limitations of proprietary technologies.

The Internet is composed of a variety of networks employing a variety of different networking technologies. They are linked by bridges which translate messages from one into a format that can be understood by another. Similarly computers from both Apple and Sun Microsystems now mimic Microsoft's Windows operating system sufficiently well to run many Windows programs. Such translations and emulations are never as good as the real thing, but they are steadily making it easier to switch from one technology to another.

The size of today's mature computer markets makes it increasingly hard to justify rationally the widespread belief that the only computer markets worth competing for are those created by the dominant technological standard. Although new technologies will still be dominated by the quickest innovators – and those who have managed to jump on their bandwagon – the mainstream should relax into diversity. The king is dying. Long live the kings to come.

Part 2

A–Z

ABDUCTION

A form of reasoning which derives premises from conclusions. For example, if you know that "if it rains, then the ground is wet" you could use DE-DUCTION to conclude that the ground is wet from the knowledge that it rains, but you could abduce that it rains from the knowledge that the ground is wet. People use abduction all the time, but it is not, as logicians love to point out, logically sound. The relation between premise and conclusion is looser than vice versa. Although it is certain that rain will wet the ground, there could be other reasons why the ground is wet: because of a sprinkler, for example, or flooding.

ACK

Short for acknowledgement, it symbolises a code sent in many communications protocols to denote that the recipient has received and understood the message. (Contrast to NACK.)

ACTIVE X

A set of standards created by MICROSOFT for down-loading small programs over the WORLD WIDE WEB that will extend the capabilities of a WEB BROWSER. An Active X control might, for example, create an animation or do specialised tax calculations. Active X controls can be written in almost any pro-gramming language. But this flexibility has not headed off a running battle between backers of JAVA and proponents of Active X over security.

Java runs in a protected environment called a "sandbox", which limits the damage a malicious Java program might do. Java programs, for exam-ple, cannot delete files that they themselves have not created. Active X, by contrast, has no such lim-itations. A malicious Active X program could quite merrily wipe out the entire contents of your HARD DISK, or worse. To demonstrate just how tricky a rogue Active X application could be, hackers from Germany's Chaos computer club built and publi-cised a game which also surreptitiously checks to see if the user of the computer it landed on used any of the more popular programs to pay bills electronically. If so, it adds a new entry to the list of bills to be paid – an account controlled by the hackers in Switzerland.

Java proponents argue that this is exactly why Active X should be avoided. Microsoft argues that its security can be guaranteed by a DIGITAL SIGNATURE system. By placing an electronic signature on Active X programs, trustworthy companies (like Microsoft) vouch for their safety. Java backers reply that knowing who to sue after you have been robbed or vandalised is poor consolation, particularly when it is easy to avoid the damage in the first place. Perhaps the best compromise, for those who worry about security but still want the capabilities Active X can offer, is simply to use only Active X controls written in Java.

ADA

A programming language developed by the USA's Department of Defense. Until 1997 Ada was required for Defense Department projects, then it was made merely "preferred", reflecting the language's notable lack of popularity. It was named after Ada Lovelace, daughter of Lord Byron, who became the world's first computer programmer when she helped Charles Babbage to construct his "difference engine", a computer made of brass gears and cogs, in the 1840s. The lady was reputed to be elegant; the language was designed by a military-industrial committee.

Charles Babbage's difference engine, designed between 1847 and 1849, had 4,000 parts. It weighed about 3 tons, and was 7 feet high and 11 feet long. It was never completed.

ADSL

Short for Asynchronous Digital Subscriber Loop, a proposed technology for sending video and other high-BANDWIDTH DATA over existing copper wires running to homes and businesses, without investing billions in upgrading basic infrastructure to FIBRE OPTIC. ADSL assumes that most homes and businesses will consume far more data than they produce. So although it manages to send over 6m BITS of INFORMATION per second into the home, it does so by restricting the amount that can be sent in the other direction. This makes ADSL suitable for showing films, but not for video-conferencing.

AGENT
A much-ballyhooed piece of SOFTWARE that will do its master's bidding without direct supervision, even remotely, over a NETWORK. For example, an agent will find travel information without requiring its owner to know anything about electronic AIRLINE RESERVATION SYSTEMS. In practice this is easier marketed than done.

AI
See ARTIFICIAL INTELLIGENCE.

AIRLINE RESERVATION SYSTEMS
The first computer systems in business which not only improved efficiency, but also provided a tighter grip on customers. In the late 1980s airline reservation systems gained the distinction of being the first computer systems to be regulated under US anti-trust law. Their history provides an intriguing study of the changing role of information technology in business.

The first airline reservation system was created jointly by American Airlines and IBM in the 1960s to increase the efficiency with which American could track its highly perishable inventory of seats. American quickly realised that, if it could put its reservation terminals on to the desks of travel agents, it could capture an exclusive distribution channel. But so did other airlines, which began to compete for the privilege of wiring travel agents. Travel agents, in turn, played one airline off against another, and accepted those terminals offering them access to the broadest range of flights for least money.

Instead of exclusivity, airlines consoled themselves with marketing bias: presenting their flights first in the list, for example, or making reservations on other carriers harder to confirm. At this point, after complaints from airlines which had not developed reservation systems, US federal regulators promulgated strict rules governing bias in the presentation of reservations information.

Meanwhile, with the advent of price and route deregulation in the 1970s, airlines began mining their reservations systems for the market information needed to construct increasingly elaborate pricing structures with more and more special fares, each aimed at a smaller subsection of the flying public. Today the big airline reservation systems – notably American Airlines' Sabre and United's Apollo – are run as arm's length subsidiaries. In some years they have made more money than the airlines which spawned them.

A-LIFE
See ARTIFICIAL LIFE.

ALGORITHM
A step-by-step recipe for performing some calculation or decision process; what computer programs are made of.

ALPHA
Preliminary version of SOFTWARE or HARDWARE, a working prototype. It is buggier and more preliminary even than BETA.

AMERICAN STANDARD CODE FOR INFORMATION INTERCHANGE
See ASCII.

AMPLITUDE
The strength of a communications signal, which is easiest to visualise as the height of the electromagnetic wave.

ANALOGUE
Describes a signal which varies smoothly and continuously over time, as opposed to DIGITAL, which describes a signal encoded as a sequence of on-or-off, one-or-zero, BITS. Analogue signals are

capable of more subtle and faithful reproduction than digital, particularly for music, voice or other signals which naturally vary smoothly and continuously. They are also, however, harder to transmit and to reproduce. Digital signals can be reproduced perfectly through the use of error correction. Analogue signals cannot; they suffer from NOISE and degradation.

To take advantage of the best qualities of both digital and analogue, many machines convert between the two. Compact disks, for example, store digitally encoded music and convert it to an analogue signal to be sent to the speakers. Telephone systems increasingly transmit digital signals and convert to and from analogue at the earpiece or receiver.

One way of doing this is to convert at some point the strength, or AMPLITUDE, of the analogue signal into a BINARY number, and vice versa. The problem, however, is that these binary approximations themselves take time to create and to transmit, while the original analogue signal varies continuously. So the process is much like trying to reproduce the flow of a curve with a collection of rectangles. The height of the rectangle represents the amplitude of the signal, while the width represents the time needed to transmit the digital number. Much effort and technology has been devoted to "blurring" digital signals into realistic and accurate analogue ones.

AND

Describes an operation in BOOLEAN ALGEBRA, often embodied as an electronic circuit, which returns 1 (or on) if, and only if, all of its inputs are 1 (or on). Otherwise it returns 0 (or off).

ANTI-VIRAL

A program that can detect, and sometimes eliminate, computer viruses.

APPLE

The company that invented the first commercially successful PERSONAL COMPUTER (PC). In 1976 Steve

Jobs and Steve Wozniak began building Apple I computers in the garage of Mr Jobs's parents' home in Cupertino, California, and selling them to fellow computer hobbyists for $666 apiece. Their next model, the Apple II, launched in 1977, was the first PC to sell beyond the hobbyist market. By 1981 its success had inspired IBM to create its own rival PC, and Apple's fortunes began a long and largely self-inflicted decline.

Apple's answer to IBM's PC was the MACINTOSH, launched in 1984 amid growing corporate strife that in 1985 saw Mr Jobs ousted by John Sculley, who Mr Jobs had recruited from soft-drinks-maker Pepsi to bring experienced management to his fledgling firm. The Macintosh was a technological marvel. Its GUI set standards for ease of use that rivals spent a decade striving to emulate. But SOFTWARE for the run-of-the-mill tasks like word processing was scarce, and Mr Sculley's insistence on high profit margins kept prices high.

Apple's market share shrank steadily through the 1980s. Mr Sculley was himself ousted in 1993, after disappointing initial sales of the product he had championed as Apple's next great gadget, the Newton PDA, or personal digital assistant. Macintosh prices were cut and market share recovered, at least until manufacturing problems brought on another drop in market share and the departure of Mr Scully's successor, Michael Spindler. Yet another crisis resulted in the departure of Mr Spindler's successor, Gil Amelio. Sadly, for all its innovation and its perennially heroic efforts to get itself out of whatever mess it stumbled into, Apple still seems likely to go down in the history of the computer as the great might have been.

Steve Wozniak sold his prize possession to finance development of the Apple I computer: his Hewlett Packard calculator. Steve Jobs sold his VW minibus.

APPLET

Either an extremely simple, small APPLICATION or, more usually, a software program written in JAVA

---

for distribution over the WORLD WIDE WEB.

APPLETALK

APPLE's proprietary technology for creating local area networks with MACINTOSH computers. The company released a faster version of Appletalk, called ETHERTALK, for use on ETHERNET networks.

To correct a manufacturing error, Apple recommended to buyers of the Apple III computer that they lift the machine a couple of feet from a hard surface and drop it.

APPLICATION

Describes a WORD PROCESSOR, SPREADSHEET, accounting program or other piece of SOFTWARE which does useful work directly for the end user. SYSTEMS SOFTWARE, by contrast, includes programming languages, OPERATING SYSTEMS and other things needed to build and to run applications software.

APPLICATION LAYER

That part of the SEVEN LAYER REFERENCE MODEL which concerns the formatting of DATA on the screen, the proper conventions for FILE names and other aspects of translating from the technical conventions of one computer system to those of another, on the other side of the NETWORK.

ARCHIE

A tool for locating SOFTWARE and technical INFORMATION on the INTERNET. Over the years the Internet has accumulated vast resources of computer software. After all, this is where researchers and students share their ideas for new technologies and hackers vie with each other to show who can write the coolest code. The problem was that finding what you wanted could sometimes be more trouble than writing the program again from scratch, at least until Archie came along. It searches for software by name across the NETWORK and then reports what is where.

ARPANET

Grandfather of many of today's large-scale computer networks, particularly the INTERNET. The Arpanet began in 1969 as a research project led by the Defence Advanced Research Projects Agency, from whose acronym, DARPA, the NETWORK derived its name. The goal was to create a computer network capable of supporting the USA's defence through a nuclear war. This meant that the network could not have a central switch or authority which could be pre-emptively destroyed. Taken together with the decision to encourage the researchers building the network to use it to share INFORMATION, this lack of central structure meant that the Arpanet could, and did, evolve into more or less whatever size and shape its denizens desired; in this case, the Internet.

A brilliant chess move while the room is filling with smoke because the house is burning down does not show intelligence. If the capacity for brilliant chess moves without regard to life circumstances deserves a name, I would naturally call it "artificial intelligence".
Anatol Holt

ARTIFICIAL INTELLIGENCE

The quest to make machines that can think as intelligently as people. Conceived in the mid-1950s, artificial intelligence (AI) raised high hopes when computers began to make relatively rapid progress in solving LOGIC problems and learning to play chess. Those hopes were rapidly punctured, however, by the realisation that the hard things to teach a computer were not the achievements on which humans pride themselves – such as logic, mathematics and chess – but common sense things which they take for granted. Computers cannot reliably navigate across a room, understand a children's story, or take a telephone message.

The problem is that logic, mathematics, chess and the like have well-defined formal rules which, given a good deal of labour, can be expressed in terms a computer can understand; day-to-day life does not. Philosophical arguments over whether or not computers ever will equal human performance centre on the SYMBOL PROCESSING HYPOTHESIS.

Today, active areas of AI research include:

- knowledge representation – that is the task of putting facts and knowledge into a machine;
- PLANNING;
- MACHINE LEARNING;
- DISTRIBUTED AI;
- reasoning – or teaching computers to use knowledge to create new knowledge, for example, by DEDUCTION.

More practically, 40 years of AI research have created many technologies sufficiently robust and useful to go to work in business, including:

- EXPERT SYSTEMS;
- NEURAL NETs;
- VISION;
- LANGUAGE UNDERSTANDING.

The techniques of artificial intelligence are to the mind what bureaucracy is to human social interaction.
Terry Winograd

ARTIFICIAL LIFE

The quest to make machines which can act as intelligently as insects. Instead of trying to understand the world, as people do, artificial-life (A-life) researchers reckon it is better to try to build machines that can simply react to it, without conscious reflection, as ants and slugs presumably do. Rodney Brooks of the Massachusetts Institute of Technology, a leader in the field, argues that a more practical alternative to a robotic butler, say, might be a horde of "ant-bots" which scurry across the floor at night picking up dust in the same way that real ants pick up crumbs. Although such creations are a long way off, if they are ever to arrive at all, studies in A-life have deepened understanding of how simple components can in

A

combination give rise to great (and possibly useful) complexity. More practically, genetic algorithms enable computer programs to mimic biological evolution in adapting to their environment.

ASCII

Pronounced *as-key*, the American Standard Code for Information Interchange, a STANDARD for encoding the characters of the Roman alphabet (that is, a, b, c, and so on) as numbers which can be stored and manipulated by a computer. Alternative character-encoding schemes include EBCDIC.

ASSEMBLER

Or assembly language, the native language of computers. The nouns and verbs of assembler correspond directly to the functions of a specific MICROPROCESSOR chip; for example, adding two numbers, or extracting a number from MEMORY. In the 1960s and early 1970s most SOFTWARE was written in assembler. But the detail required caused delays and errors. Today programs are more easily written in higher-level languages – such as ADA, C and COBOL – which are automatically translated back into their assembler equivalents (by a COMPILER) for execution on the computer.

ASYNCHRONOUS

Not having the same time clock. Most communications technologies assume that the clocks of sender and receiver can tick at different rates. This means that they have to include ways of communicating where each part of the signal starts and stops, to avoid, for example, the receiver taking the last half of the code for the letter a and the first half of the code for the letter z to come up with the letter o. For most purposes it is easier to send start and stop signals than to keep the two clocks precisely synchronised. (Contrast to SYNCHRONOUS.)

ASYNCHRONOUS DIGITAL SUBSCRIBER LOOP
See ADSL.

ASYNCHRONOUS TRANSFER MODE

The fastest of a new breed of telecoms switches. Like other PACKET switching devices, asynchronous transfer mode (ATM) routes DIGITAL DATA divided into small chunks, each a few BYTEs long, called packets. Key to their speed is that ATM packets are all of a uniform size – 53 bytes – of which 48 are data. The remaining 5 bytes carry INFORMATION about that data, notably its destination (to distinguish the many different transmissions that might be sharing a communications channel) and its priority (to distinguish, say, a videoconference, whose packets must arrive quickly, from a piece of E-MAIL, which can be delayed for a few milliseconds if necessary). Using ATM technology, researchers hope to build switches that can transmit data at speeds of gigabits per second, an order of magnitude or two faster than today's networks. That would make it as quick to send information across a NETWORK as to move it around within a single computer. In a very real sense, ATM could make vast networks act as a single computer cum telephone cum television cum…

ATM

See ASYNCHRONOUS TRANSFER MODE. This is also the acronym for automated teller machine: the hole-in-the-wall which dispenses bank notes on the insertion of a plastic card.

AUTOMATION

Doing a task automatically, without human intervention, usually by entrusting the work to a machine. The point of automation is typically to dispense with human skills, because they are either expensive, or untrustworthy, or both. Many applications of information technology differ from traditional mechanisation in that they require people to be kept in the LOOP, but using somewhat different skills, and doing somewhat different work, than they had done before (see INFOMATION).

B-TREE
A method of structuring DATA so that it can be accessed quickly. It is most often used for files stored on DISK, but it can be used for any collection of data that can be put into some order.

BACK-UP
To save a copy of DATA stored on a DISK on to another medium, usually tape or OPTICAL DISK. Backup is meant to provide a reserve copy of data lest something terrible should happen to the disk.

BACKWARD CHAINING
See EXPERT SYSTEM.

BANDWIDTH
Loosely, the amount of INFORMATION or DATA communicated: a high-bandwidth communication is, or should be, more informative than a low-bandwidth one. Strictly, bandwidth refers to the difference between the highest FREQUENCY that a given communications channel can carry and the lowest. Channels in which this difference is large can carry more data than those in which it is small. Indeed, given a strict mathematical definition of information, Harold Nyquist, a theoretician from the USA's Bell Labs, proved in 1924 that the maximum number of BITs a channel could carry was equal to twice the bandwidth.

BASIC
Beginner's All-purpose Symbolic Instruction Code, an easy-to-learn programming language popular on the PERSONAL COMPUTER. Now increasingly superseded by more powerful languages like C.

BAT
A suffix which denotes to MICROSOFT's DOS OPERATING SYSTEM that the FILE bearing it contains a SCRIPT, that is, a set of commands that the operating system should execute in order to automate a simple task. The file called *autoexec.bat* is executed automatically when the computer is first started, and is thus used to initialise and to customise the system.

BATCH PROCESSING

Describes a computer system which works to a rigorous and uninterruptable schedule. Jobs, for example a payroll, are scheduled for the hour when the computer next has free processing time. Once started, the job runs to completion. Interactive computers, by contrast, try to reschedule work on an ad hoc basis to respond to urgent and unexpected demands. Historically, most MAINFRAME computers have used batch processing, which is largely responsible for their reputation as being inconvenient and annoying.

BAUD

A measure of the speed of DIGITAL communications equipment which is closely related to the maximum number of BITs that can be sent in a second.

BAYESIAN ANALYSIS

A form of statistics which calculates the probability of some event given knowledge of some related INFORMATION. For example, conventional statistics enable the calculation of the (small) probability that a given person has measles at any given moment. Bayesian statistics calculate the (larger) probability that the person has measles, given the knowledge that he is covered in spots. Named after the 18th-century British mathematician, Thomas Bayes, this technique is widely used in automated diagnosis (for obvious reasons).

BETA

The final stage of SOFTWARE quality testing. Before general release, selected people are typically given beta copies of software to use as if it were finished in order to see what, if anything, breaks.

BINARY

Loosely used to describe anything without shades of grey; that is, which can be either black or white, true or false, on or off. Strictly, it refers to a number system based on the number two. Instead of powers of ten, as in the DECIMAL system, numbers are expressed in terms of powers of two. The only allowable digits are zero and one. Thus 27 in decimal ($2 \times 10^1 + 7 \times 10^0$) is 11011 in binary ($1 \times 2^4 + 1 \times 2^3 + 0 \times 2^2 + 1 \times 2^1 + 1 \times 2^0$). This number system is convenient for describing electronic circuits, which are either on (with current) or off (without).

BIND
To associate a value with a variable.

BINHEX
A program to convert BINARY files into ASCII ones that can be sent over the INTERNET, most commonly used on MACINTOSH computers.

BIT
Short for binary digit, thus zero or one (see BINARY).

BIT MAP
A grid of dots which contains the information needed to display a picture on a computer screen or PRINTER. Typically each dot corresponds to the colour of a particular point, or PIXEL, on the screen. Display the dots in the appropriate rows and columns and, lo and behold, a picture appears. (The colour of dots, in turn, is coded as BITS, hence the name.)

This correspondence between dots in the bit map and points on the screen makes bit maps easy to use on any given screen. But it also makes them extremely hard to move from one screen to another, because different screens lay out rows and columns in different proportions. (See also VECTOR GRAPHICS, of which the converse is true.)

BOOLEAN ALGEBRA
Provides a theoretical understanding of how computers compute. In the 19th century the British mathematician, George Boole, studied in detail formal rules for calculating with the values true and false, which underlie formal LOGIC. His work remained relatively obscure until the 1960s, when someone noticed that the true and false of Boole's logic correspond to the on or off of an electrical switch, and that Boole's rules of calculation could

be used to understand better how those switches could add, subtract and calculate.

BOOLEAN EXPRESSION
A series of true or false propositions connected by the logical operations AND, OR or "not".

BOOT STRAP
Or boot, refers to the initial stages of starting up a computer. Usually the OPERATING SYSTEM loads programs from DISK into MEMORY. So what loads the operating system? The boot strap code, of course, which runs when the power is first turned on.

BRIDGE
Equipment used to connect two local area networks. Bridges can connect networks using different communication protocols (for example, TCP/IP and APPLETALK), as well as different transmission mechanisms (for example, ETHERNET and TOKEN RING). A ROUTER, by contrast, is used to connect networks with the same PROTOCOL.

BRITTLE
Describes computer systems that break suddenly and completely. A common fault of many programs, particularly ARTIFICIAL INTELLIGENCE programs, is that they work either perfectly or not at all. This is usually a bad thing. (Contrast with GRACEFUL DEGRADATION.)

BROADBAND
Loosely used to describe signals of high BANDWIDTH. It is specifically used to describe the use of (high-bandwidth) COAXIAL CABLE to transmit radio, television or other ANALOGUE signals that would typically be sent over the airwaves. Also used as a generic term for high-speed telecommunications circuits and services.

BROADCAST
Describes a signal sent indiscriminately to all receivers with range, such as television, in contrast to point-to-point communication (such as a tele-

phone), or person-to-person communication (such as conversation). With computer networks researchers are developing new forms of communication, between broadcast and point-to-point, called MULTICAST.

BUFFER

A section of computer MEMORY, typically one used for temporary storage. A communications buffer, for example, acts as a kind of marshalling area for DATA coming into, or going out of, a computer.

BUG

An error or problem with computer HARDWARE or SOFTWARE. It is named after a moth, discovered by a computing pioneer, Grace Hopper, which immolated itself in the circuitry of an early computer. The computer was repaired by replacing a damaged vacuum tube. The moth is preserved in the Computer Museum in Cambridge, Massachusetts.

BULLETIN BOARD

A computer system used for posting electronic messages. Messages are organised into files on the bulletin board's HARD DISK, usually by topic. People can dial up the bulletin board and read what has been said on a given topic and, if they like, add their own comments. Little more is required to run a bulletin board than a PERSONAL COMPUTER and MODEM. By the early 1990s the USA alone had over 50,000 public bulletin boards.

BUS

The central wiring that connects together the components of a computer.

BYTE

Eight BITS, the most commonly used measure of DATA-storage capacity. Large HARD-DISK drives, for example, store gigabytes (that is, billions of bytes) of INFORMATION. A nibble is half a byte, or four bits.

C

The most popular programming language for personal computers and workstations. Created in the 1970s at Bell Labs by Dennis Ritchie, C was originally distributed with the UNIX OPERATING SYSTEM. It owes its popularity to its ability to express the nitty-gritty details of a computer's inner workings (to help achieve efficiency) with a certain elegance and abstraction (to help achieve comprehensibility by mere flesh and blood).

C++

An OBJECT-ORIENTED successor to C created by Bjarne Stroustrop at Bell Labs in the 1980s. Its name is a programming pun. To add one to a variable (say n) in C, a programmer would write $n++$. Hence C++ (for the one after C). Who says programmers don't have a sense of fun?

CABLE MODEM

A MODEM built to take advantage of the high BANDWIDTH available on the COAXIAL CABLE laid to distribute television signals. Cable modems can achieve data-transmission speeds equal to that of ETHERNET, or around 10m bits per second.

CACHE

A small area of very fast MEMORY, typically on a MICROPROCESSOR, which is used to store (what the machine hopes will be) the next instructions used in the computation, and thus to eliminate delays by making them available more rapidly than if they had to be fetched from the main DRAM.

CAD

Short for Computer Aided Design. SOFTWARE which helps draughtsmen and graphic artists. Computers can greatly simplify the task of keeping technical drawings in the proper scale and perspective. They can manage libraries of ready-drawn objects, and, like word processors, computer-aided design programs greatly simplify the task of making alterations.

CALL CENTRE

A centralised facility for handling customer enquiries over the telephone. It is a far more interesting place than it sounds. The technology of call centres is at the cutting edge of the integration of computers and communications. When someone calls, their telephone number is snatched automatically from the line and looked up in a DATABASE. If someone calling from that number has done business with the company before, all details are on screen when the call is answered. Meanwhile, in the background, a marketing analysis program compares that customer's purchases with those of its fellows to see what this customer might want to buy next, and then to prompt the salesperson into suggesting it.

This integration between computers and communications inspires many CIOs to see in them the future of office AUTOMATION. Not all of those who work with the technology will see this as a blessing. The automation can empower workers by putting INFORMATION at their finger-tips, but it can also turn them into script-following drones. All it takes is a slight push of management emphasis either way.

CALS

Short for Computer Aided Logistics and Support, an ambitious program led by the USA's Defense Department to set the standards necessary to automate military procurement. In theory, the standards cover all stages of production: bidding, design, manufacturing and documentation.

CAM

Short for Computer Aided Manufacturing, a generic term used to refer to AUTOMATION on the shop floor.

CARRIER

The carrier is a constant signal into which information is encoded, typically by varying the carrier's FREQUENCY, AMPLITUDE, or both.

CASE

Short for Computer Aided Software Engineering, that is, SOFTWARE which helps programmers. There are a variety of computer-aided software engineering tools. Some help keep track of different versions of an evolving program. Others help to find bugs. Yet others make it easy to design and build forms on screen for entering and displaying DATA. A FOURTH-GENERATION LANGUAGE simplifies the task of writing programs that use a DATABASE.

CASE-BASED REASONING

Techniques in ARTIFICIAL INTELLIGENCE, originally devised by Janet Kolodner of the Georgia Institute of Technology, which reason from precedent. In effect, the technology builds an electronic DATABASE which describes previous situations encountered and records the action taken then. When a new situation is met, the computer tries to find a past situation sufficiently similar that the same action will work again. The difficulty, of course, is defining similar. But Compaq, among others, has successfully used the technology to build up corporate databases which help newcomers to share the knowledge of their more experienced colleagues.

CASTANET

A technology for creating PUSH MEDIA, created by members of the team that created JAVA. Marimba, the company that built Castanet, originally saw the technology as a way of distributing SOFTWARE upgrades across networks, but soon realised that software was just another form of information.

Unlike Pointcast, which began by creating a network to distribute INFORMATION as a service, Marimba focused from the beginning on creating technology for people to distribute information on their own. It has been used to send news to commercial subscribers, to update employees on company policies and to distribute software updates.

CCITT

The French acronym for the International Consultative Committee for Telegraphy and Telephony, a group set up by United Nations treaty to set technical standards for the world's communication systems. Most countries are represented by their PTT. CCITT is most well-known in the computer world for the V STANDARDS and other standards used in DATA communications.

CDF

Short for Channel Definition Format, used to create PUSH MEDIA. The CDF specifies how to describe what information the channel contains and what has changed since each user's last update, so that each subscriber can get the information he needs, and only the information he needs.

CDMA

Short for Code Division Multiple Access, a way of multiplexing a variety of signals on to a single communications channel. CDMA first makes several copies of each BIT to be transmitted. Then it combines each expanded group of bits with a special code, of the same length, and transmits the result. Many other transmitters may be sending their own (expanded and coded) signals on the same channel. So, at the other end, the receiver picks up all transmissions, effectively added together. But using the special code it can pick the signal it wants to listen to out of the jumble.

CDMA uses BANDWIDTH more flexibly than its chief technical rival TCMA, but there is less experience in using it. Europe and the USA are trying to choose between the two for the next generation of wireless telephones and DATA networks.

CD-ROM

Short for Compact Disk, Read-Only Memory, the medium of choice for the first generation of MULTIMEDIA publishers. Compact disks, the same kind as are used for sound recording, can store a lot of DATA – about 640 megabytes, 600 or so times more than a FLOPPY DISK. That is enough to store the text from several hundred books, two hours of high-quality sound, an hour of television-quality video, or some combination of the above.

CELLULAR AUTOMATA
A mathematical creation useful for simulating complex, dynamic phenomena. Cellular automata are based on a grid of cells. Each cell contains a value. At each step of a computation, each cell calculates a new value based on the values of neighbouring cells. (For example, 1 if the sum of the values of surrounding cells is less than 4; otherwise 0.) Even simple rules can spawn immensely complex behaviour. With highly parallel computers to help with the computation, researchers are using cellular automata to improve their understanding of phenomena ranging from the flow of fluids to foetal development, all areas in which (presumably) simple local interactions create global behaviour of great complexity.

Adding manpower to a late software project makes it later.
Fred Brooks, 1975

CELLULAR TELEPHONE
A wireless mobile telephone. The name refers to the overlapping NETWORK of radio receivers required to provide service to a mobile telephone. Each receiver's reception area is called a cell. For technologists, the tricky part of building mobile telephone networks lies in ensuring a seamless hand-off for moving users (say in a car) as they move from one cell to another. For business planners, the trick is ensuring a sufficient capacity for a whole country (or indeed region) full of constantly moving subscribers.

CENTRAL PROCESSING UNIT
See CPU.

CGI
Short for Common Gateway Interface, a PROTOCOL used to enable programs to work together over the WORLD WIDE WEB. CGI links executable programs

to Web pages. So, instead of just sending text in response to each click of the MOUSE on a HYPERTEXT link, some links can run programs to make calculations or make new pages on the fly, perhaps by running a query on a DATABASE to find up-to-the-second information.

CHANNEL DEFINITION FORMAT
See CDF.

CHECKSUM
A way of detecting errors in computer DATA. The BINARY values of the data are added together to form a checksum. The checksum is transmitted with the data. If the sum of the binary values of the received data differs from the received checksum, then something has gone wrong.

CIM
Short for Computer Integrated Manufacturing, which describes efforts to link CAD to electronically controlled machine tools to enable designers simply to push a button and, whoosh, designs are automatically translated into machining instructions, and thus into real parts.

CIO
Short for Chief Information Officer, a job which brings together responsibility for corporate INFORMATION and knowledge with responsibility for managing the technology which stores and communicates it. In theory, CIOs are perfectly positioned to lead corporate change; in practice, their jobs are also highly insecure.

CIRCUIT SWITCHED
How a telephone works. When a connection is made, sender and receiver have the BANDWIDTH of the intervening line all to themselves for the duration of the connection, whether they use it or not. (Contrast with PACKET SWITCHED.)

CISC
Short for Complex Instruction Set Computing, an

approach to the design of microprocessors, popular in the 1970s, which tried to pack as many functions as possible into the instruction set, or set of commands which that MICROPROCESSOR could understand. Unfortunately, the complexity of creating all these instructions slows chips down, and studies showed that few of them were used anyway. So CISC has been superseded by RISC, a minimalist approach to chip design.

CLIENT SERVER
Describes computer systems which divide labour among machines linked by networks. Rather like Adam Smith's pin factory, each machine does what it is suited for. So a FILE SERVER is equipped with lots of DISK space to store DATA; a name server holds the information necessary to serve as the NETWORK's telephone directory. Not only does specialisation avoid duplication of effort, but it also makes client-server systems easier to improve. If, say, all heavy-duty number-crunching is done by a calculation server, then simply replacing that one machine with a more powerful one can improve the performance of the whole network.

CMOS
Short for Complementary Metal Oxide Semiconductor, a way of making a SEMICONDUCTOR with low power consumption. CMOS chips are often used in laptop computers and other battery-powered devices.

COAXIAL CABLE
The thick wire through which cable television and other high-BANDWIDTH signals travel (also called coax). The thickness comes from an extra layer of metal mesh wrapped around the copper-wire core, to guard against electrical interference.

COBOL
Short for Common Business Oriented Language, a computer language designed for business use in the 1960s. It is now the world's most used programming language. Its verbose structure, created

to read like English, creates a mandatory mediocrity, making it as hard to write really bad programs as it is to write really good ones.

COMMAND-LINE INTERFACE

Describes a computer which provides a prompt, or command-line, for the user to type in commands. This is in contrast to a MENU-DRIVEN INTERFACE, which asks the user to choose from a menu of commands displayed on the screen. Command-line interfaces, like that offered by MICROSOFT's DOS, offer users great flexibility, but they require them to remember the exact magical incantations which will induce the computer to act. Menu-driven interfaces, like the MACINTOSH, are easy to use – particularly for those not terribly familiar with the system – but harder to customise or to do complicated things with.

COMMON CARRIER

A communications company which carries information for all. It also refers to regulatory regimes designed to ensure non-discriminatory access to communications networks.

COMPILER

A piece of SOFTWARE which translates programs written in high-level languages like C and COBOL into the MACHINE CODE which computers can act upon. Using a compiler, creating and running a program requires two separate steps. First the compiler translates the source code into a separate FILE of machine code, often optimising as it does so to make the program run as fast as possible. Then the computer runs the programs by executing the instructions in this separate machine code file. This is in contrast to an INTERPRETER, which does the job in a single step, translating and executing the source code itself. Interpreted programs run more slowly than compiled ones, but they are quicker and easier to DEBUG.

COMPOSITE MONITOR

A colour MONITOR that mixes together red, green

and blue signals for ease of input, and thereby suffers somewhat inferior resolution compared with an RGB MONITOR.

COMPRESSION
Techniques for reducing the amount of DATA needed to convey some amount of INFORMATION. (See, for example, RUN-LENGTH ENCODING, LZW ALGORITHM, HUFFMAN CODING.)

COMPUTER AIDED DESIGN
See CAD.

COMPUTER AIDED LOGISTICS AND SUPPORT
See CALS.

COMPUTER AIDED MANUFACTURING
See CAM.

COMPUTER AIDED SOFTWARE ENGINEERING
See CASE.

COMPUTER INTEGRATED MANUFACTURING
See CIM.

COMPUTER SUPPORTED CO-OPERATIVE WORK
The use of computers to help people work together more productively. Computer supported co-operative work (CSCW) divides into two broad categories. GROUPWARE is typically used to share INFORMATION among a group. WORKFLOW prompts users through a complex task, reminding them at each step of the way what should be done next.

Although the distinction is not always clear-cut, groupware, like decision-support systems, exists largely to help people make up their own minds. The assumption is that, given the right information, they are knowledgeable enough to make the right decision. Workflow systems, by contrast, assume that the machine knows best.

CONNECTIONIST
Describes computing done with a NEURAL NET. In general, connectionists argue that – in silicon as in

the human brain – it is complex connections and feedback between individual computing units (or neurons) that give a machine the power to tackle complex problems, not the raw capabilities of any one.

If the Internet's present 100% a year rate of growth continues, everyone on the planet will be connected by 2003.

COOKIE

A common but somewhat convoluted way of gathering and storing INFORMATION about WORLD WIDE WEB users. It is DISK-space-consuming and complicated for a Web site to store on its own computers all the information it might want about its users. So it uses cookies, which store and retrieve the same information on users' computers.

Say a Web site wants to track which of its pages a particular user visits most. It sends the user a message called a cookie, which contains both the usage information to be stored and some indexing information. The WEB BROWSER stores the information in a FILE name suggested by the cookie. Next time the user visits the site, the site asks for the cookie back, and so gets back up to speed with what the user has been doing. Because cookies can, and often do, contain personal information they create huge worries about privacy. The OPEN PROFILING STANDARD was created specifically to give users more control over what their cookies say about them.

CORBA

Short for Common Object Request Broker Architecture, a would-be STANDARD to enable OBJECT-ORIENTED programs to co-operate over networks. To print a document on a LASER PRINTER today, a person has to find the available printers and pick one. CORBA would enable a document automatically to send out a query across the NETWORK to find the available printer which best suited its needs. (See also OLE and OPENDOC.)

CORE
An antiquated term used to refer to computer MEMORY.

CPU
Short for central processing unit. The brains of a computer; the chip or chips that execute programs.

CRACKER
A malicious HACKER; someone whose joy in life is breaking into other people's computer and communication systems and then trashing them.

CRASH
A verb or noun describing what happens when a computer ceases to function. It derives from DISK crash, which describes what happens when the magnetic heads designed to read information from a disk drive instead bury themselves into it. Synonyms for crash include wedged, down, hosed, sucking mud, hung, catatonic, in Helen Keller mode and others too descriptive to print.

CRC
See CYCLIC REDUNDANCY CHECK.

CSCW
See COMPUTER SUPPORTED CO-OPERATIVE WORK.

CURSOR
An ICON, often an arrow, which marks on the screen the focus of attention of a computer program. Text typed at the keyboard will be inserted at the location of the cursor in the text. Clicking the MOUSE will select the item pointed to by the cursor.

CYBERNETICS
The science of control systems, from thermostats to auto-pilots. Developed by Norbert Wiener at the Massachusetts Institute of Technology in the 1940s, one of the central themes of cybernetics is the notion of feedback, the idea that a system's past can affect its future. Negative feedback is

what a thermostat does: the more heat there was in the past, the less there will be in future. Population growth is governed by positive feedback: the more bunnies there are today, the more the population will grow tomorrow.

CYBERSPACE

The virtual geography created by computers and networks; the world behind the screen. Perhaps the most vivid vision of cyberspace comes from William Gibson. In his science-fiction novel *Neuromancer* – which for many is the defining vision of the techno-future – he describes, quoting from an imaginary children's show being transmitted across the NETWORK of the future, a virtual world in which DATA is made visible, and the network becomes geography:

> *Cyberspace. A consensual hallucination experienced daily by billions of legitimate operators, in every nation, by children being taught mathematical concepts... A graphic representation of data extracted from the banks of every computer in the human system. Unthinkable complexity. Lines of light ranged in the nonspace of the mind, clusters and constellations of data. Like city lights, receding...*

CYCLIC REDUNDANCY CHECK

A brain-bogglingly complicated calculation which is used to detect errors in DATA being sent over communications lines.

DAEMON

A program which sits unobtrusively in the background waiting for some event to happen, which it then deals with. In the UNIX OPERATING SYSTEM, for example, daemons handle the delivery of E-MAIL and other NETWORK requests.

DATA

Raw facts, which are not necessarily relevant to anything anybody wants to know; INFORMATION, by contrast, is data that answers a question.

DATA DICTIONARY

A list of all the different sorts of DATA contained in a computing system, including details of standard formats, how they are stored on the computer and what they represent.

DATA ENCRYPTION STANDARD

See DES.

DATA-LINK LAYER

That part of the SEVEN LAYER REFERENCE MODEL which concerns technologies for error correction and access to the underlying communications medium. Technologies working at the data-link level try to create the illusion of a perfect, error-free transmission line for the packets that come and go across it. Different approaches use a variety of methods to detect and correct errors.

DATA MINING

Techniques for sifting through huge quantities of DATA, typically using powerful computers, to try to find INFORMATION, typically in the form of either statistical correlations or rare facts. A common use of data mining is for market segmentation, to break customers down into ever-more specific categories so that their needs can be precisely catered for. Another is in the detection of fraud, detecting the subtle patterns that distinguish legitimate use from theft.

Inevitably, the power of data mining carries dangers. In any large collection of data there are likely to be more spurious, coincidental correlations than real ones. In one set of World Bank statistics, for example, the statistic which most closely tracks the US stock market is butter production in Bangladesh. The naive assumption that any strong correlation is worth a new business plan will surely lead to grief.

DATA MODEL

A formal description of the sorts of DATA a computer system should keep on any given subject. For example, the data model for a customer might include name, address and age. Although they sound simple, data models are rapidly becoming highly complex because different people want to know different things. To be assigned to the team building a corporate data model is to be given a Sisyphean task, unlikely to be finished before your career has run its course.

DATA PROTECTION

Refers to regulation concerning the privacy of DATA, typically personal data. Most countries require companies which hold INFORMATION about their customers to divulge what information they have and how they got it. Many further require companies to register their information holdings with a data protection board, which is charged with looking after citizens' interests. None of these solutions really work, though. All seem to be bureaucratic, ineffective, or both. So data protection and privacy will continue to be one of the most heated issues in the regulation of CYBERSPACE.

DATA WAREHOUSE

A DATABASE which brings together in one place INFORMATION from different systems working in different parts of a company. Often that DATA is further supplemented with additional information from outside the company. Data warehouses typically serve two purposes. One is to provide a wide range of data for analysis. Retailers, for example, use data warehouses to devise marketing strategy – to understand the statistical patterns in customer purchases and so to present the right product to the right customer at the right time. Another is to help create more flexible companies by making it easier for different departments to share information. This not only improves cooperation; it also makes it easier to shift work and responsibility between departments, as changing circumstances require.

DATABASE

A computerised filing system which forms the core of most corporate computer systems. Databases store and retrieve INFORMATION, and as the number of different kinds of information kept on computers increases, databases are evolving to cope.

The most common database now in use is the RELATIONAL DATABASE. A few banks still use a HIERARCHICAL DATABASE, but most are struggling to convert to the newer relational technology. For the future, developers are working on the OBJECT DATABASE, which makes it easier to store video, graphics and other complex data alongside the sorts of text and data that most databases now contain.

Each database also has a query language, which allows its users to access its data. The most popular one nowadays is STRUCTURED QUERY LANGUAGE.

DBMS

Short for DATABASE Management System.

DEBUG

To correct errors in a computer program (see BUG).

DECIMAL

Describes the number system based on counting by tens which most people use every day. (Contrast to BINARY and HEXADECIMAL, the number systems which most computers use every day.)

DECISION-SUPPORT SYSTEM

A computer system designed to provide the INFORMATION needed to help people make up their minds, as distinct from an EXPERT SYSTEM, which is a computer system designed to make up people's minds for them. The advantage the computer can bring to decision support is that it can provide information either more quickly than would otherwise be possible, or in greater detail, or both.

DECLARATIVE PROGRAMMING

A style of programming that allows the programmer to concentrate on what is to be done, without worrying too much about how. PROLOG is a good example of declarative programming. It allows programs to be written as a DATABASE of facts, supplemented by statements about those facts. The program computes by trying to make those statements true, and in theory the programmer does not have to worry too much about how it does so. By contrast procedural programming languages like C and LISP require the programmer to state exactly the procedures the program is to follow, step by detailed step.

DEDUCTION

Reasoning which proceeds from premises to conclusions. Typically, deduction involves both facts and rules of reasoning. Given, for a simple example, the rule "all men are mortal" and the fact "Fred is a man", then we can deduce "Fred is mortal". (See also ABDUCTION and INDUCTION.)

DEEP BLUE

A computer built by researchers at IBM which in 1997 defeated the reigning human chess champion, Gary Kasparov. Deep Blue owes its chess-playing prowess to its ability to examine hundreds of millions of possible positions, rating each by simple criteria like pieces lost or won, not to any understanding of the strategy of the game. This inspired some cynical comments from John McCarthy, a leading ARTIFICIAL INTELLIGENCE researcher at Stanford University. He wrote:

In 1965 the Russian mathematician Alexander Kronorod said "Chess is the drosophila of AI". However, computer chess has developed as genetics might have if the geneticists had concentrated their efforts on breeding racing drosophila. We would have some science, but mostly we would have very fast fruit flies.

DES
Short for Data Encryption Standard, originally created for use by the US government. Unlike PUBLIC-KEY CRYPTOGRAPHY, DES keys must be exchanged before encrypted messages can be decoded.

DESKTOP PUBLISHING
Describes HARDWARE and SOFTWARE for personal computers that can lay out text and graphics at a fraction of the cost of a large publishing house, but with quality nearly as high.

There is no reason for any individual to have a computer in their home.

Ken Olsen, founder of Digital Equipment Corporation, 1977

DIGITAL
DATA stored as a sequence of discrete BINARY digits, as opposed to analogue, which is data stored as a continuously varying signal. (See ANALOGUE for a discussion of the pros and cons of each.)

DIGITAL SIGNATURE
A cryptographic technique which ensures that an electronic document really does come from the person whose name is at the top. Strictly, a digital signature has two functions: it serves as proof of identity, like a regular signature, and as proof that the document has not been tampered with.

Implemented with PUBLIC-KEY CRYPTOGRAPHY, the workings of the signature parts are straightforward. All or part of the document is encrypted with an individual's PRIVATE KEY, which is (or should be) known only to him. That text can only be decrypted with the corresponding public key.

Ensuring that a document has not been tampered with relies on a HASH FUNCTION, which condenses the text into a short but unique series of numbers. When the document is received, it is checked to ensure that the hash function returns the same numbers.

Crucial in making this scheme work is ensuring that public keys really do come from who they purport to. Some governments propose to license a network of trusted third parties to do this job. Unfortunately, many also propose that these trusted third parties should be required to hold the corresponding private keys – which they have no need to do for digital signatures – and to hand them over to the police on demand so that encrypted messages can be tapped. This would seem to make them highly untrustworthy third parties. (See also TRUSTED THIRD PARTY.)

DIGITAL VERSATILE DISK
See DVD.

DIMM
Short for Dual In-line Memory Module. DIMMs are a way of packaging MEMORY chips for ease of installation. As the name implies, DIMMs allow twice as much DATA to be written to memory at each tick of the processor's clock as their predecessors, SIMMs (64 BITs instead of 32 bits). INTEL'S PENTIUM processor requires DIMMs to move data fast enough to keep up with its speed.

DISK
A medium for the storage of DATA. Most disks now in use are magnetically coated, and store the 1s and 0s of DIGITAL data by imprinting (or not imprinting) a tiny magnetic field on the disk. Optical disks work on a similar basis with a laser and a reflective (or non-reflective) coating. (See also OPTICAL DISK, FLOPPY DISK and HARD DISK.)

DISTRIBUTED AI
An approach to ARTIFICIAL INTELLIGENCE (AI) based on the hope that many small intelligences can do more than one big one. Traditional AI would, for

example, try to improve the flow of road traffic by creating a single supreme intelligence, which knew everything that went on the roads and tried to optimise globally. The snag is that many problems become unworkably large and complex if tackled all at once. So distributed AI tries to solve big problems as a series of small ones, each tackled by a different problem-solving agent.

Given this approach, distributed AI inevitably shifts the emphasis of research. Instead of trying to eke the most out of each problem-solver, the distributed approach tries also to find ways for problem-solver agents to co-ordinate their efforts via negotiation, co-operation and delegation.

DISTRIBUTED COMPUTING
The practice of using different computers, linked across a NETWORK, to solve computing problems co-operatively. (Contrast with MAINFRAME and see also CLIENT SERVER.)

DOMAIN NAME
A NETWORK address. To save the trouble of typing gibberish numbers like 195.92.40.6, the INTERNET is organised as a collection of named domains. Each DOMAIN name serves as a mnemonic way of referring to a specific set of network numbers.

Domain names, like domains, are typically arranged in a hierarchy. At the most general level of the hierarchy are country names, like .uk, or sectoral names, like .gov for government. Next come names referring to a specific institution within that general sector, then names referring to parts of the company and lastly a name referring to a specific machine.

Administering domain names has become one of the most controversial aspects of Internet management. One problem is to sort out the links between domain names and trademarks. When, for example, can a company sue to recover a domain name which resembles its trademark? Another is deciding who has the authority to administer domain names. Should it be an international body, national bodies, and, if both, how will the dividing lines be drawn? Until 1997, at least, domain names were administered nationally. But pressure has grown to create international administration for a global technology.

DOS

Short for Disk Operating System, MICROSOFT's OPERATING SYSTEM for desktop computers. Originally incarnated as QDOS, for quick-and-dirty operating system, DOS was written by Tim Patterson at Seattle Computer Products. Bill Gates bought the rights to the program for $250,000 when he discovered that IBM, which had approached him to license his implementation of the BASIC programming language, might also be interested in an operating system. The rest is history.

DOT MATRIX PRINTER
See MATRIX PRINTER.

DOUBLE-PRECISION ARITHMETIC
FLOATING-POINT ARITHMETIC, performed with a large number of bytes in order to try to preserve accuracy, despite the inevitable ROUNDING ERRORS which stem from trying to fit numbers with potentially unlimited digits beyond the decimal point into a limited number of bytes in the computer.

DOWNLOAD
To transfer DATA from a remote (usually large) computer to a local (usually small) one. (Contrast with UPLOAD.)

DRAM

Short for Dynamic Random Access Memory, the MEMORY chips used by most computers. DRAM stores BITS as tiny electric charges on a grid of tiny circuits. Each bit's charge (or lack of charge) can be accessed independently, by specifying the row and column of the circuit on which the charge is held, hence random access. But to keep costs down, charge is held in such a way that it gradually dwindles if left on its own and thus must be constantly refreshed (hence dynamic). This refreshing cycle makes DRAM slightly slower than SRAM (static RAM), but the extra nanoseconds are considered well worth the cost saving.

Today DRAM is usually sold mounted on SIMMs or DIMMs for convenience of use. By 1997 chips with 64 megabits of storage had become widely available and research labs were producing 256 megabit chips, which is a lot of memory when many PCs are sold with 32 megabytes of DRAM.

DUAL IN-LINE MEMORY MODULE
See DIMM.

DUMP
To record verbatim, without any attempt to order, usually for archival purposes; roughly the computer's equivalent of stream of consciousness.

DUPLEX
A communication channel which allows messages to travel in both directions at once. (Contrast with SIMPLEX.)

DVD
Short for Digital Versatile Disk, a higher-capacity replacement for CD-ROM. DVD disks hold a minimum of 4.7 gigabytes – eight times more than a CD-ROM and enough to put a full-length film on a single DISK. Better, the technology of DVD can create disks holding up to 17 gigabytes of data. Best of all, DVD drives will play previous CD formats, including CD-ROM and music CD.

The fly in the DVD ointment, though, is the copy-protection technology built into commercial players at the insistence of Hollywood film studios. It is understandable that Hollywood should worry about copying of digital work because an infinite number of perfect copies can be made of any digital video. But there is no need to worry about ANALOGUE video, the quality of which deteriorates with each copy. Furthermore, Hollywood has added to its copy-protection scheme technology which prevent DVDs produced for the US market from being played in Europe or Asia.

E1 LINE

A standard European LEASED LINE, which offers 2.048 million BITs per second of data-transmission capacity. The American equivalent is the less capacious T1 LINE.

E3 LINE

A standard European LEASED LINE, which offers a data-transmission capacity of 34 million BITs per second. The American equivalent is a T3 LINE.

E-MAIL

Short for electronic mail. Just as the name implies, a message sent electronically from one computer to another. E-mail is typically text, but emerging standards for MULTIMEDIA mail, notably MIME, enable anything that can be put in DIGITAL form to be e-mailed. Roughly a fifth of the traffic on the INTERNET consists of e-mail.

EBCDIC

Abbreviation for Enhanced Binary Coded Decimal Interchange Code, a STANDARD for coding text characters as numbers used on IBM mainframes. Almost as complicated to use as it is to say, EBCDIC is being superseded by ASCII and other more modern character codes.

EDI

Short for Electronic Data Interchange, the automatic, electronic exchange of corporate DATA, particularly boring, nitty-gritty things like parts orders, manufacturing instructions or inventory data.

EISA

Abbreviation for Extended Industry Standard Architecture, a standard BUS to carry DATA between the MICROPROCESSOR of an IBM-COMPATIBLE PERSONAL COMPUTER and MEMORY, disks and other peripherals. EISA will accept HARDWARE add-ons created for the ISA bus of the original IBM PC, but, given more capable equipment, it can also carry more data faster than the original.

ELECTRONIC FRONTIER
A phrase coined by a writer and activist, John Perry Barlow, to describe the challenge of creating laws and customs to govern CYBERSPACE.

EMACS
Short for Editing Macros. Created by a legendary HACKER, Richard Stallman, EMACS is probably the most popular WORD PROCESSOR for the UNIX OPERATING SYSTEM.

EMERGENT PROPERTY
An interesting and useful side-effect of a complex system. It is possible – perhaps common – for a system to achieve collectively goals which none of its components aim at individually. Economists, for example, have shown that, under many conditions, market competition provides a globally optimal distribution of resources, even though all the market participants are trying simply to get as much for themselves as they can.

ENTERPRISE REQUIREMENTS PLANNING
See ERP.

ENTITY-RELATIONSHIP MODEL
An approach commonly used in SYSTEMS ANALYSIS which, as the name suggests, maps out the sorts of things a computer system might have to represent and the relationships between them. An entity-relationship model for a library card catalogue, for example, might describe an entity called a book. The entry for book might further be linked to a person's name, with a relationship of author.

EOF
Short for End Of File. The name says it all really.

EPROM
Abbreviation for Erasable, Programmable, Read-Only Memory, a chip that can store DATA indefinitely (like any other ROM) but that can be erased and reprogrammed; unlike some forms of ROM which, once programmed, are fixed forever.

ERP

Short for Enterprise Requirements Planning, describing programs which help plan optimal production, order raw materials, and so on. It is much like MRP (Materials Requirements Planning), but has a potential market sufficiently larger to inspire some marketing departments to adopt a new acronym.

ESCAPE CHARACTER

A special character to denote that the character to follow has a special meaning. For example, an escape character followed by the letter c on some computer systems interrupts a program; while c alone is just c.

ETHERNET

A form of LOCAL AREA NETWORK, originally invented by Robert Metcalfe of Rank Xerox's Palo Alto Research Laboratory. It differs from a TOKEN-RING NETWORK chiefly in the way in which it mediates access to the network. In a token-ring network, computers constantly pass around an electronic token, and they can send DATA only if they hold the token. In Ethernet, by contrast, computers can send data any time they do not hear another computer already sending. If two send simultaneously, the collision is detected (because the data is garbled), and the two each wait a random period of time before trying again. In most circumstances Ethernet's *laissez-faire* approach is more efficient than token-ring's rigid discipline, except when network traffic is heavy. Most first-generation Ethernets transmitted about 10m BITs per second. Next-generation "fast" Ethernets transmit up to 100m bits per second.

ETHERTALK

A fast version of APPLE's proprietary APPLETALK technology for local area networks, which, as the name suggests, works on ETHERNET.

EXE

A suffix which denotes executable files (that is,

programs) in the DOS OPERATING SYSTEM.

EXECUTIVE INFORMATION SYSTEM
A DECISION-SUPPORT SYSTEM for executives.

EXPERT SYSTEM
A computer system that tries to capture the knowledge of a human expert. This knowledge is typically stored as a series of if-then rules: for example, an expert system to diagnose computer faults might include the rules, "if the computer is unplugged, it has no power" and "if the machine has no power, then the screen is dark".

Large expert systems, with more than a hundred rules, rapidly become unwieldy. But miniature decision-makers can serve a variety of useful roles. They are used to help keep blast furnaces running smoothly in steel mills; to enable photocopiers to diagnose their own faults and dial a repairman; and to advise welfare applicants on which benefits they may be eligible for.

In the mid-1980s, when expert systems burst into the commercial world, many claimed that the systems would soon replace many skilled workers. They have not – and will not. Like *idiots savants*, the machines are totally incompetent outside their narrow realm of expertise. They can advise on the minutiae of, say, sickness benefit, but they have no idea of what it is to be sick. So expert systems are most useful when working closely with a real person. The machine can help the person to remember details; the person can bring the machine's expertise to bear on the real world.

EXTRANET
Another word that has lost much of its meaning since its appropriation by the marketing departments of major SOFTWARE and computer manufacturers. Strictly, an extranet is a NETWORK, built using the INTERNET's technical standards, which links two or more different companies but is not open to the general public. Contrast to the wholly private INTRANET and the wholly public Internet.

FAQ

Short for Frequently Asked Questions. For many of the topics under discussion on the INTERNET, particularly on a USENET NEWS GROUP, it is customary to maintain a beginner's guide, answering the most frequently asked questions on the topic. (For example, the FAQ for the news group *alt.sex* answers questions like: "What are some good positions to try out?" and "Can I be replaced by a vibrator?") Newcomers with NETIQUETTE read the FAQ before asking a question that may have been asked and answered a thousand times before; others get a FLAME.

FDDI

Short for Fibre Distributed Data Interface, a high-BANDWIDTH LOCAL AREA NETWORK which uses FIBRE-OPTIC cable to transmit DATA at up to 100m BITs per second, ten times the speed of ETHERNET.

FIBRE OPTIC

A fine glass fibre which transmits light, much the same as a copper wire transmits electricity. Because it can be switched on or off extremely rapidly – much faster than an electric current – fibre optic can carry far more DATA than conventional copper wire.

FIDONET

A global computer NETWORK created for and by users of personal computers. Like USENET, FidoNet was a store-and-forward network; messages hopped from machine to machine, each sending the message a step nearer its destination. FidoNet has now largely been absorbed by the more technically sophisticated INTERNET.

FIELD

A component of an entry in a DATABASE. The INFORMATION in a database is composed of records, which in turn are composed of fields. Each RECORD corresponds to an individual entry, such as information about a particular customer. That record will be made up of a collection of fields, each containing a particular piece of DATA. For a customer record, for example, fields might well include name, date of birth, sex, and so on.

FIFO

First In, First Out, a method of managing incoming and outgoing DATA. FIFO dictates that the first piece of data to arrive will also be the first to be used. Although data may be stored temporarily in a BUFFER should more come in than can be immediately processed, FIFO guarantees that data will be processed in the order in which it arrives, in contrast to LIFO, which usually changes the order. In accounting FIFO and LIFO are methods used for valuing inventory.

FILE

The organising unit of a computer DISK. Computer files are by intention roughly analogous to the sort found in a filing cabinet: a collection of (presumably logically related) information stored together under a single name.

FILE SERVER

A machine on a NETWORK whose job it is to store files of DATA for other, linked computers. Typically the file server has more DISK space, and faster technology for accessing it, than other machines. Storing files centrally avoids duplication and makes administration easier.

FINGER

The name of a program used to get information about a computer user over a NETWORK. On the INTERNET, for example, typing *finger bloggs@somewhere.com* will usually produce a list of the full names and E-MAIL addresses of everyone named *bloggs* on the *somewhere.com* network.

FIREWALL

HARDWARE, but more usually SOFTWARE, designed to protect networked systems from damage by outsiders, while maintaining connectivity. The firewall sits between a local NETWORK and the big, wide world (usually the INTERNET). To protect the local network from unwelcome intruders, the firewall may admit only designated users, or allow only designated commands to be issued from outside. Balancing flexibility with SECURITY is a perennial headache in designing firewalls.

FIRST IN, FIRST OUT
See FIFO.

FLAME
A rude and abusive electronic communication. Electronic communication seems to lend itself to extreme forthrightness, perhaps because typing at a screen provides much of the emotion-raising interactivity of a conversation, but none of the interactive cues that signal when the person you are typing to is about to hit you, or cry. Outbursts of mutual forthrightness on networks are called flame wars, and are generally discouraged.

FLAT FILE
A DATA FILE with only minimal structure. To speed access, many DATABASE technologies carefully structure the data in files so that the particular INFORMATION can be located on the DISK as quickly as possible (see, for example, B-TREE). Flat files have no such structure, and are thus typically quicker and cheaper to write information to, but slower to read from.

FLAT-RATE PRICING
The sort of pricing scheme used by most INTERNET service providers (ISPs). Instead of charging by the minute, as telephone companies have traditionally done, most ISPs charge only a fixed rate each month, no matter how long users stay ONLINE or how much DATA they send.

FLOATING-POINT ARITHMETIC
Arithmetic done with what mathematicians call REAL NUMBERS, that is, numbers with a decimal point in them. (Contrast with INTEGER arithmetic.)

A perennial problem with floating-point arithmetic is loss of precision. Some real numbers theoretically require an infinite number of digits to the right of the decimal point; 1 divided by 3, for example. Many more require more such digits than can fit into the slice of computer MEMORY allocated to store a representation of the number. Over time these ROUNDING ERRORS compound each other, making computer calculations wildly inaccurate if the problem is not overcome.

FLOPPY DISK

A portable form of computer DISK, used to record fairly small quantities of electronic DATA. Floppy disks originally consisted of a round piece of cardboard, coated with a magnetic recording material similar to that used in recording tape. They were soft and floppy, hence the name. More modern, higher-capacity floppy disks are made of magnetically coated plastic, and they are in fact quite stiff. But somehow the word stiffy has never caught on as a replacement for floppy.

FLOW CHART

A kind of blueprint for building a computer program. Flow charts represent graphically not only the actions taken by a program as it executes, but also the choices it makes.

FLOW CONTROL

Procedures to manage the flow of DATA across a computer channel, typically to ensure that the receiving computer is not flooded with more information that it can handle. One commonly used method of flow control is XON XOFF, which sends a special signal, XON, to start transmission and another, XOFF, to interrupt it.

FORTH

A programming language which views the world through computer-coloured glasses. Specifically, it requires that programs be written in terms of stacks, a way of organising the work of calculation that is convenient for computers. It comes naturally to some people but apparently not enough to make Forth a really popular language, like C.

FOURTH-GENERATION LANGUAGE

A programming language, often linked directly with a specific DATABASE, which tries to provide ready-made tools to do common tasks, like laying out a screen or printing a report. The hope, which is sometimes realised, is that programmers will become more productive if they can use ready-made tools instead of building their own. The problem, however, is that the ready-made tools often do not do what is required and so must be time-consumingly modified. At the same time, the computing resources required by fourth-generation languages can make programs large and slow; another failed panacea.

FORTRAN

Acronym derived from Formula Translation, an early programming language created at IBM and particularly suited for mathematical number-crunching, for which it is still used.

FRAME PROBLEM

One of the classic problems in ARTIFICIAL INTELLIGENCE (AI), the frame problem concerns limiting the consequences of actions. When we say, for example, "the boy hit the ball", we instinctively assume that, while the ball moves, objects not mentioned – the cap on the boy's head, for example, or the shoes on his feet – stay the same. Or at least the cap and the shoes do not move as far as the ball does. One of the nastier aspects of the frame problem is that deciding what changes matter to the description of the problem is often highly subjective. Worse still, instinctive assumptions involve deep issues about the "connectedness" of things which are hard to translate into a form that a computer can understand.

Today's solutions to the frame problem are frame axioms which state explicitly what each action changes and what it does not. But these solutions in turn raise their own problems. First, they add bulk and complication to AI's descriptions of the world. Second, they are hard to get right. Predicting the consequences of actions can be tricky, and frame axioms can introduce errors and contradictions of their own.

FRAME RELAY

A PACKET switching PROTOCOL, typically used for a WIDE AREA NETWORK, which can transmit data at up to 2m BITS per second. Although much faster than most LEASED LINES, which provide tens or hundreds of thousands of bits per second, this is still much slower than a LOCAL AREA NETWORK, which generally carries about 10m bits per second.

FREQUENCY

The rate of oscillation of a communications signal. It is typically measured in HERTZ, or cycles per second.

FRONT OFFICE

That part of the business that deals directly with the customer – making sales, marketing, and so on. Although computers began their career in the back office they are moving to the front office with the advent of order-entry systems, marketing information published on the WORLD WIDE WEB and sales people carrying laptops.

FTP

Short for File Transfer Protocol. This refers to both the program which transfers files from one computer to another across the INTERNET, and the technical standards it uses. Bulk transfers of DATA with FTP make up about one-third of Internet traffic.

FUNCTIONAL PROGRAMMING

Programming languages, like LISP, which are based on a mathematical theory of functions. The hope is to do away, as far as possible, with the variables in which conventional programs store values. The snag with variables is that, if one part of the program sets, say, x equal to 5, there is no guarantee that another part of the program will not have set it to 7 by the time it is next used, with potentially unpredictable results. Functional programming tries to overcome this by not storing values but by calculating each one afresh with a new function (which is simply something that calculates and returns a value). A snag with this approach, however, is that calculating each value afresh can consume huge quantities of time and/or MEMORY.

FUZZY LOGIC

A formal method of DEDUCTION which substitutes various shades of maybe for the stark, true-or-false choice of classical LOGIC. Take, for example, fat. In predicate logic, people either are fat, or they are not; there is no middle ground. So if a computer is to reason about fatness, its programmer has to devise an arbitrary weight at which people go from being non-fat to being fat. Fuzzy logic, by contrast, enables a computer to reason in terms of degrees of fatness, more like people do.

Not surprisingly, it typically works with percentages. Instead of an arbitrary threshold value at which somebody becomes fat, each possible weight is assigned a percentage value which indicates just how fat it is. At one extreme, fashion models would be 0% fat; towards the other extreme, Santa Claus might be, say, 90% fat; while only people with severe medical problems are 100% fat. These percentages will inevitably be somewhat arbitrary. The real advantage of fuzzy logic is not its (in)ability to quantify the unquantifiable, but its ability to reason with it.

At the heart of fuzzy logic are rules for reasoning with the percentages that denote the fuzzy categorisation of objects. Various approaches have been proposed for the task of combining "sort of fat" with "sort of short" to determine whether or not a person could be considered "short and fat". The solutions turn out to be particularly valuable for creating control systems for small appliances, such as washing machines, which have to figure out how to behave when confronted with a "pretty small" load of "quite dirty" clothes.

G

GATEWAY
A device that connects different computer systems or networks, particularly those using different technical standards or communications protocols.

GEEK
Like a NERD, someone who has devoted time to technology at the expense of more normal life. As technical knowledge has become fashionable, a new breed has arisen: the chic geek.

> *There are no bad haircuts in cyberspace.*
> Dave Barry

GENETIC ALGORITHM
A rough equivalent of Darwinian selection – survival of the fittest – used to breed SOFTWARE that is suited for a particular task. There are two basic components of any genetic algorithm: some measure of fitness, or success at a given task, and some analogue of breeding, whereby old software creates new software that behaves somewhat like its parents and somewhat differently. The basic procedure is to test a collection of programs on the task at hand, measure their fitness, and then allow only the fittest to breed. Given that computers can breed several generations in the blink of an eye, evolution proceeds quickly inside the machine. Genetic algorithms have bred successful solutions to many problems, including picking investment opportunities and monitoring suspicious financial transactions.

GEOSTATIONARY
Describes a satellite whose orbit is so synchronised with the rotation of the earth that it effectively hovers over the same spot. This property is useful for communications satellites, because the ground stations always know where to point their transmissions, and, once found, the satellite never moves out of range. But the positions where geostationary (GEO) satellites can be located are already growing crowded.

GIF
Short for Graphics Information File, a widely used STANDARD for the format of the DATA needed to store images in a computer FILE. (See also JPEG, TIFF and PICT.)

GIGA-
Strictly, the prefix denotes a billion. In the computer world, however, it refers to 1,073,741,824, the nearest power of two.

GIGO
Short for Garbage In, Garbage Out, a pithy way of saying that the quality of the answers a system can give depends on the quality of the information given it to reason with. Truer words …

Computers are useless. They can only give you answers.
Pablo Picasso

GLOBAL POSITIONING SYSTEM
See GPS.

GLOBAL SYSTEM FOR MOBILE
See GSM.

GNU
Short for Gnu's Not Unix, which is the sort of self-referential pun beloved of computer programmers accustomed to writing programs which can recursively call themselves to get work done. It is the brand name of a collection of programs created by Richard Stallman and his fellow hackers at MIT. They replace, and in some cases improve upon, the standard components of the UNIX OPERATING SYSTEM, including compilers and NETWORK utilities.

GOPHER
A collection of programs that make it easier to find information on the INTERNET. While TELNET and FTP require knowledge of specific FILE names and computers, Gopher can find material by subject

category. Named after the school mascot of the University of Minnesota, where it was developed, Gopher is still widely used but has been over-shadowed by the growth of the WORLD WIDE WEB.

GPS
Short for Global Positioning System, a satellite-based system which can determine the location of someone on the ground to within a few hundred metres. Originally developed for the military, GPS is rapidly finding civilian use, particularly as the necessary transceivers are shrinking to palm size. Someday your palm-top computer may be able not only to recommend the nearest Chinese restaurant in a strange city, but also to guide you to it.

GRACEFUL DEGRADATION
Describes resilient machines or systems that do not break all at once, but keep soldiering on even if some components are broken. (Contrast with BRITTLE.)

GRAMMAR
A formal specification of the SYNTAX of a language, programming or human. It includes the parts of speech and the order in which they can be put together to create "correct" statements. Note that grammatically correct sentences need not make any sense whatsoever. SEMANTICS is concerned with meaning, grammar is not.

GRAPHICAL USER INTERFACE
See GUI.

GROUPWARE
SOFTWARE that helps a group of workers to share the knowledge needed to co-operate in doing their jobs. The technology became popular through a product called Notes, created by Lotus Development, and was sufficiently successful to inspire IBM to buy Lotus to get its hands on the program. At the heart of Notes are discussion databases, which enable workers to share INFORMATION. The basic capabilities of these

databases are quite simple, but their impact on business processes is potentially vast because they enable workers to access simultaneously information which previously they could only hand on to the next person in rigid sequence.

Notes databases are typically organised like correspondence files. Under each subject heading come various contributions, which will include not only E-MAIL but also other electronic documents including spreadsheets, DATABASE reports and text from word processors.

Such information-sharing capabilities have proved themselves useful in situations where companies need to bring diverse skills and knowledge to bear on a single task. Qantas uses Notes to help marketing and operations work together in devising flight schedules; Manufacturer's Hanover uses the technology to bring together the pieces of giant international loans; Lotus uses Notes to help sell Notes; and international management consultancies use the technology to capture the expertise of consulting teams spread across the world.

But there is far more to groupware than Notes. There are more structured forms of the technology, specialised to suit specific tasks. Some products help a group of writers to manage collaboration on a joint text; others work with CAD systems to help engineers work together on design projects. Meeting-support software is designed to help groups of managers get the most out of meetings. However, the greatest growth, and the threat to Notes's early dominance of groupware, is in intranets. Using Web browsers, e-mail and other software, many companies find that they can electronically enhance internal communications far more cheaply and flexibly than with Notes. Not only are INTRANET solutions a fraction of the price of Notes, but they can also be more easily extended to take on new sorts of communications or to include new discussion members, both in the company or elsewhere in the world.

A problem with all of these forms of electronic teamwork is that groups of people interact differently when communicating electronically from when they are face-to-face. In general, electronic communication is a leveller. For better and worse, it breaks up the bonds of social hierarchy which hold groups together. It makes it easier to brainstorm but harder to reach consensus. Many MEETING SUPPORT SYSTEMS rely on a human facilitator to help move groups towards agreement; in other applications groupware often accompanies a shift towards more independent, empowered styles of working. For having given workers all the information needed to make up their own minds, it is hard to stop them from doing so.

GSM

Abbreviation for Global System for Mobile communications, the European STANDARD for DIGITAL mobile telephones.

GUI

Short for Graphical User Interface, pronounced *goo-ey*. Strictly, a GUI is any computer that communicates with its user using pictures as well as words. In practice, most GUIs today build on work originated at Xerox's Palo Alto Research Center (PARC), which has four key elements.

- **WINDOW.** Instead of a single screen, the computer screen is separated into several different areas, each independent of the others. Each window might display a separate program, or a distinct view of the same program.
- **ICON.** Instead of describing programs and DATA with names, today's GUIs often use pictures. A WORD PROCESSOR might be represented by a pen, for example.
- **MOUSE.** Instead of typing commands to a program, GUIs enable a user to move a pointer, or CURSOR, around the screen using a device called a mouse.
- **MENU.** Instead of forcing the user to remember the handful of magic words which programs understand, GUIs present

choices from a list of options (which typically appears in its own window).

The earliest popular computer to embody these ideas was APPLE's MACINTOSH, which, when it appeared in 1984, was greatly inspired by visits to Xerox PARC. The Macintosh organises its screen as a virtual desktop. Files are represented as filing folders. Documents can be dropped into them for safe-keeping. Alternatively, files or folders can be dropped into a wastebasket for deletion. Since the Macintosh, similar ideas have been used to create interfaces for a variety of other systems, notably MICROSOFT's WINDOWS for IBM-COMPATIBLE computers and X-WINDOWS for UNIX machines.

Two challenges will define the next generation of GUIs. The first is to incorporate the NETWORK into the desktop, to make remote information as accessible as local, to represent active agents as well as passive objects like files, and to cope more gracefully with new sorts of objects like Web pages. Particularly on big networks, a computer may be juggling several tasks at once, and new interfaces will have to keep users informed of the progress of all of them, interrupting if necessary yet not becoming intrusive. By 1997 most major SOFTWARE companies were launching next-generation GUIs which incorporate JAVA into the OPERATING SYSTEM and extend the desktop metaphor to include Web pages as well as local files and programs.

The second challenge is to represent ever more complex data. The computer is no longer a window on to just the desktop, but on to the whole corporation and the world around it. Xerox PARC is experimenting with three-dimensional interfaces which represent on the screen, say, the familiar layout of the workplace. You can "walk" the screen to, say, accounts for accounting information and marketing for marketing data. On Wall Street, by contrast, others are experimenting with the use of VIRTUAL-REALITY headsets to represent, in three-dimensional graphics, information which might help a securities trader to decide what is hot and what is not.

HACK

A neat piece of programming, often inspired by the need to solve or work around a specific problem. Also what a HACKER does.

HACKER

Strictly, a hacker is a skilled and dedicated programmer, who, in the words of *The New Hacker's Dictionary*, "enjoys exploring the details of programmable systems and how to stretch their capabilities, as opposed to most users, who prefer to learn only the minimum necessary". But the word has also recently come to connote a benign kind of computer prankster, dedicated to achieving unauthorised entry into, say, NASA's mission control computers, just to say he was there. (Contrast with CRACKER and PHREAKER.)

> *An experienced hacker was sitting next to a neophyte who was trying to fix his jammed terminal by turning the power off to reset the software. "Don't you know that you can't fix a computer just by cycling the power without knowing what's really going on?" said the hacker. Then he turned the power on and off, and the machine worked.*

HALTING PROBLEM

One of the fundamental theories of computer science, the halting problem is not really a problem but refers to a proof that demonstrates the impossibility of creating a computer program which can determine whether any other program will eventually reach an answer. (Of course this is easy for some programs, but not for all programs.) In effect, the halting problem demonstrates that some things cannot be computed.

HANDSHAKE

A PROTOCOL used to co-ordinate the activities of two computers. They might engage in a handshake to acknowledge each other's presence on a NETWORK ("I'm here." "Yes, I see you; talk to you later.").

HANDWRITING RECOGNITION

Techniques for teaching a computer to read human handwriting. In theory, a computer should be able to analyse shapes and sequences of letters to guess words. In practice, most handwriting proved too irregular for PDAs to live up to their initial hype.

HARD DISK

Or Winchester drive, after one of the inventors of the technology. This is a fixed, rigid DISK, typically permanently installed within a computer. Like a FLOPPY DISK, it is made by coating magnetic material on to a disk. But the rigid construction of hard disks means that they can be rotated more rapidly, and that DATA can be packed more precisely into smaller magnetic markings on the disk. Faster rotation means that data can be read and written more rapidly; more precise markings mean that more data can be packed on to the disk. By 1997 hard disks of 5–6 gigabytes were quite common, while most floppies held only about 1 megabyte, a difference of many orders of magnitude.

HASH FUNCTION

Describes techniques for reducing a long stream of text or a picture to a number, which is both much shorter and, it is hoped, unique to the original DATA. It is used in indexing and DIGITAL SIGNATURE systems.

HARDWARE

Computer equipment that you can drop on your foot, assuming you could lift it in the first place. (Contrast with SOFTWARE.)

HDML

Short for Hyper Devices Mark-up Language, a version of HTML created by Unwired Planet, a small SOFTWARE house, for creating Web pages which can be displayed on mobile devices with teeny screens. Although HTML has been evolving the capabilities to mimic paper pages, with graphics and neatly formatted text, it has also become increasingly difficult to display on, say, the screen of a mobile phone. HDML, by contrast, was made specifically to work on screens as small as 12 x 4 characters, with no graphics whatsoever.

HEADER

DATA about data. Typically included at the beginning of a FILE, a document or a data PACKET sent over a communications NETWORK, the header typically contains information to identify the attached data, to state how much data is attached, what sort of data it is, how long it is and to help detect and/or correct errors.

HEISENBUG

A BUG (or defect) which is difficult to replicate or to diagnose. It is named after the Heisenberg Uncertainty Principle, which told physicists that there were limits to the accuracy with which they could measure the speed and momentum of an object: limits which only really matter at sub-atomic distances and speeds near that of light, but limits nonetheless. These limits arise because the very act of measuring an object disturbs it. Similarly, the act of observing a program in operation disturbs it.

HERTZ

A measure of FREQUENCY named after the German scientist Heinrich Hertz: one cycle per second.

HEURISTIC

A rule of thumb. It refers to computations which rely on human wisdom and experience to solve problems, rather than a formal, mathematically rigorous ALGORITHM. A rule-based EXPERT SYSTEM, for example, is commonly based on heuristics learned by interviewing human experts.

HEXADECIMAL

A number system which counts by 16s instead of the tens usual in the DECIMAL system. This is convenient for describing the contents of computer

MEMORY, because two hexadecimal digits correspond to a single BYTE, in contrast to decimal numbers, which do not fit so neatly. Counting by 16s, however, requires new digits to represent the numbers 10–15, which is by convention done with the letters A–F. (See also BINARY.)

HIERARCHICAL DATABASE

A now largely outdated form of DATABASE which, as the name suggests, organises information in a hierarchy. If, for example, the database was to store information on the employees of the parks department, it might first categorise them by job: gardeners, street sweepers, tree surgeons, and so on. Then it might list names under each category, and addresses under each name, and so on.

This scheme of organisation turns out to be quite quick and easy for a computer to manage, and because of its speed the technology was adopted by many banks. But it also has two large drawbacks. First, it is quick only so long as the database is looking up information within a single hierarchy, such as finding a gardener's address. It becomes slow and clumsy when trying to compare the addresses of all employees. Worse, not all data are created equal. So if employees no longer fit into an established category – say because they are on sick leave – they disappear from the database altogether. For these reasons the hierarchical database has largely been replaced by the RELATIONAL DATABASE.

HIGH ORDER

The most significant (those furthest to the left when the number is written out) BITS of a BINARY digit. As fiddling with the hundreds digit in 124 is a bigger change than fiddling with the ones, so changing the high order bits creates a bigger change than changing the LOW ORDER ones.

HOLLERITH CARD

A computing antique. The PUNCHED CARD was originally created for mechanical calculators built in the 1880s by Herman Hollerith. He also invented a special code for writing numbers on the cards, called, not surprisingly, the Hollerith code.

HOST COMPUTER

Strictly, the computer which holds the program and/or DATA under consideration. More generically, any big computer likely to hold a lot of programs and data. (See also CLIENT SERVER.)

HTML

Short for HyperText Mark-up Language, the programming language which creates the documents and links used by the WORLD WIDE WEB. The language contains commands for laying out text and graphics on a page, as well as commands to link one document to another – or to link a document to an interactive computer program – to create HYPERMEDIA.

HTTP

Short for HyperText Transfer Protocol, the PROTOCOL used to move Web pages across the INTERNET.

HUFFMAN CODING

A form of DATA COMPRESSION, which works on the quite reasonable principle that the most commonly used symbol should have the shortest code. So instead of, as ASCII does, giving all the characters of the alphabet seven-BIT codes, a Huffman code would make the letter e the shortest – at least for English in which it is the most common character.

HYPER DEVICES MARK-UP LANGUAGE

See HDML.

HYPERMEDIA

Like HYPERTEXT, but including sound, video and other media.

HYPERTEXT

Text that need not be read from beginning to end, but can instead be browsed in any number of different orders, at the reader's whim, by following internal route-marks called links. A typical application of hypertext is in reference works, like this one. In an electronic version of this book, cross-references would not only be distinguished by special type, but they could also be "live". Click on them with a MOUSE and, whoosh, the computer brings up the appropriate entry on the screen.

Today's most popular application of hypertext (strictly speaking hypermedia) is the WORLD WIDE WEB, which uses the technology to link a vast collection of INFORMATION spread across the INTERNET. By clicking on highlighted words and pictures, net-surfers can call up a satellite photograph of the weather, or query a DATABASE of securities prices, or begin a global search for academic publications, or ... well, you name it. But hypertext is also being used in a variety of other applications. Hypertext electronic reference works are becoming common, and many are experimenting with hypertext novels. For an interesting, if somewhat pretentious, techno-literary discussion, try debating at your next dinner party the proposition: "hypertext means the death of narrative".

HYPERTEXT MARK-UP LANGUAGE
See HTML.

IBM

The world's biggest computer company. IBM (International Business Machines) is the only computer company to compete globally in all sectors of the computer market, from the MAINFRAME to the PERSONAL COMPUTER (PC). Over the course of the 1970s and 1980s it grew to four or five times the size of its nearest competitors. Then, just when it seemed invincible, IBM ran into serious trouble.

For most of its history IBM has been run by marketers and salesmen. Thomas J. Watson Sr made his career and reputation as a salesman before he was appointed in 1914 to run the Computing-Tabulating-Recording Company, when it was renamed IBM, by a Wall Street financier, Charles Flint. His son followed his path through sales to the top of the rapidly expanding company. As it moved into computers in the 1950s and 1960s, IBM's focus on the customer helped it ease fears about the new technology, and gain the widespread trust needed to lead the market.

The product that brought IBM to the top of the computer market was System/360, launched in the early 1960s. The selling point of System/360 was simply that it offered a range of computers, from big to small, that could all run the same SOFTWARE and use the same DISK drives, printers and other peripherals. So a company could start with a small machine and work up to a large one, without investing in new software or accessories.

From System/360 to the launch of IBM's PC in 1981, technology advanced quickly enough to baffle even the most intrepid consumer. IBM salespeople prospered in part by providing reassurance. "You never get fired for buying IBM." That trust, in turn, generated so much cash that IBM's Thomas J. Watson research laboratories could spend more each year on research and development than many of its competitors made in total sales. The future looked supremely rosy, but three changes created a crisis at IBM by the early 1990s.

- **IBM-COMPATIBLE PCs.** When it launched its PC, IBM decided to buy its MICROPROCESSOR from

INTEL and its OPERATING SYSTEM from
MICROSOFT, and to use an easily copied BUS to
link its computer together. Rivals could buy
the same components. The result was copy-
cat, IBM-compatible computers sold at cut
prices by companies which did not have the
overheads IBM had built up as it created the
sales, marketing and support staff necessary
to hold customers' hands. Although IBM's
technology accounted for nearly 90% of the
PCs sold, IBM itself made less than 10%.

- **Technological complexity.** By the late
  1980s IBM was increasingly hard-pressed to
  make good its promise to make the right
  technological choices for its customers.
  There were simply too many technologies
  for IBM salespeople to stay on top of,
  particularly as the company felt obliged to
  support its own aged machines as well as
  the new ones coming on to the market.
  Customers began to complain that they were
  being sold what was most convenient for
  IBM rather than what was best for them. The
  managerial procedures that IBM put into
  place to help support sales staff slowed
  down decision-making, which caused
  further dissatisfaction.
- **Customer sophistication.** As computers
  spread across corporate desktops, and the
  ability to purchase PCs fell within even
  modest budgets, more and more managers
  became comfortable with the idea of making
  their own decisions about computers
  (sometimes unrealistically comfortable). So
  customers began to look more critically at
  IBM's judgements just as technological
  complexity made it more difficult for IBM to
  make good ones.

By the early 1990s IBM was in disarray. Market
share was falling, and it made huge losses. Executives were talking about breaking the company up
into smaller, more manageable units. For the first

time since Thomas J. Watson Sr began to build the firm, IBM brought in an outsider as chairman: Louis Gerstener, a former executive of American Express, who was then running RJR Nabisco. He shelved plans to break up the firm, and began trying to find ways of combining the strength and resources of a giant firm with the nimbleness and entrepreneurial independence of a small one. He bought Lotus Development to use its Notes software to get into the burgeoning market for GROUP-WARE. He also embraced the INTERNET, pointing out that, among their other uses, IBM mainframes could create powerful and resilient Web sites. The crisis passed, but the struggle will be a long one.

IBM-COMPATIBLE

A PERSONAL COMPUTER built to run the same SOFT-WARE, and accept the same HARDWARE add-ons, as IBM's PCs. This typically means an INTEL MICROPRO-CESSOR, MICROSOFT's DOS and WINDOWS operating systems and a PCI or an ISA BUS to link the parts (although EISA and MCA buses are also used).

ICON

A graphic device, designed to make a program or FILE quickly and easily recognisable on a computer screen. What a MOUSE usually clicks on.

IDENTITY HACKING

Pretending to be someone else on a computer NETWORK. (After all, if nobody can see your face, why not?) For reasons best left to their psychiatrists, many men seem to enjoy pretending to be women on computer networks, particularly in conversations where sex is involved.

IETF

Short for Internet Engineering Task Force, the ad hoc group through which consensus is achieved on new technical standards for the INTERNET. Typically, the standards-setting process starts with a document called an RFC (REQUEST FOR COMMENTS), which lays out details of a new technology. The comments of relevant experts are then used to guide modifications of the technology until it is acceptable to all. Unlike most other international standards-setting bodies, the IETF insists that any proposed standard must first be implemented and running in prototype. This emphasis on implementation has encouraged the rapid technological development of the Internet.

IMPLEMENTATION

A real working piece of HARDWARE or SOFTWARE, as opposed to an abstract specification, sometimes used in contrast to INTERFACE.

INDUCTION

A way of reasoning about the properties of things which can be counted, or at least arranged in a sequence. Proofs by induction typically involve two steps. First prove that the first element of the sequence has the property in question. Then show that if some arbitrary element of the sequence has the property, the next element in the sequence must also have the property. If so, hey presto, all the elements of the sequence must have the property.

INFOMATION

A term coined by Soshana Zuboff, in her book *The Age of the Smart Machine*, to try to distinguish the impact of computers from traditional AUTOMATION. The key difference is the amount of INFORMATION each makes available to workers.

Automation disenfranchises workers because it breaks work down into a rigidly defined series of small steps, and, as it does so, it makes it hard for workers performing their tasks to comprehend the rest of the process. The use of computers, Soshana Zuboff argues, can (but does not always) eliminate these barriers. Sometimes inadvertently, computers enable workers to see beyond their own tasks, and to comprehend the process as a whole. At the same time, the flexibility of computer technology can enable a more flexible, ad hoc division of labour to substitute for the rigid, fixed divisions of the production line. GROUPWARE tries to make the most of the opportunities for new styles of working that computers can create.

Everybody gets so much information all day long that they lose their common sense.
Gertrude Stein

INFORMATION

Nobody has yet managed to give a really precise definition of information, which is odd considering that we are in the middle of an information revolution. Instinctively, information is useful DATA; that is, it is data that answers questions instead of just taking up space. But pinning down the notion of "useful" has proved tricky.

The first rigorous definition of information was created by Claude Shannon of AT&T's Bell Labs in 1948. It is in many ways a mathematical version of an old newspaperman's saying: "Dog bites man is not news; but man bites dog is." The reason, says Shannon, is that the information carried by an event is directly proportional to the probability of its occurring. Expected events carry little information; unexpected ones carry a lot.

Shannon used this insight to calculate the amounts of information carried by communication lines under various conditions, and to get a grip on how NOISE on the line, by obscuring parts of the signal, can reduce information-carrying capacity. But Shannon's theory has big limitations, as he was the first to admit. Because it relies so heavily on the probability of forthcoming events, it is impossible to cope with the myriad shades of meaning. Instead it views the world in terms of symbols in a communications channel, like the letters on this page. (Shannon later worked on written English and found that there were large amounts of redundancy coded into the language, often in the final letters of a word.)

Although still influential, Shannon's view of information has in some applications been superseded by an algorithmic view of information, which argues that the amount of information carried by an event is directly proportional to the smallest computer program which could reproduce the event (given some idealised computer).

INFORMATION RETRIEVAL

The task of searching for INFORMATION by subject or topic. Getting a computer to look up information relevant to some given topic turns out to be a far trickier task than it first seems. A large part of the problem lies in the sheer slipperiness of information. If you knew what you were looking for, you would not need to ask the computer.

Over the years computer scientists and librarians have devised several approaches to the problem, including the following.

- **Full-text search.** Computers can speed through the complete text of documents to find given words. The snag, however, is that such a search will often return hundreds or thousands of documents.
- **KEYWORD search.** Many books and papers are now filed by a list of words denoting the most important topics covered. This works but requires great skill and consistency on the part of the people classifying the documents.
- **Probabilistic searching.** This technique searches the full text of a document for a list of words. But not all matches are treated equally. Matches to words that occur infrequently in the overall collection of documents are considered more important than those that occur frequently in ranking matches.
- **Relevance feedback.** Having found one document that contains interesting stuff, this technique uses information from that document – keywords, infrequently occurring words, or whatever – to refine the search.
- **Parsing.** Some programs try to use ARTIFICIAL INTELLIGENCE to understand the text more or less as humans do. While the approach is

instinctively appealing, there is no evidence that it performs better than statistical techniques.

Information wants to be free; it also wants to be expensive.
Steward Brand

INK-JET PRINTER

A PRINTER which forms letters by shooting tiny droplets of ink on to the page. The heart of an ink-jet printer is a cleverly designed nozzle and ink cartridge. One wall of the ink cartridge oscillates rapidly as an electric current is passed through it, forcing a steady stream of tiny droplets out of the nozzle. On leaving the nozzle, the droplets pass through a precisely varied magnetic field, which deflects them to just the right spot on the page to form the next tiny addition to the letter or drawing under construction. Ink-jet printers offer quality of printing nearly as good as a LASER PRINTER, but for less money. They can also work on surfaces which laser printers cannot cope with, such as cloth.

INSTRUCTION SET

The complete collection of all the nouns and verbs in the assembly language for a particular MICROPROCESSOR. As the instruction set defines the basic capabilities of the chip, it determines which sorts of programs are easy to write and which are hard. In the 1970s chip designers tried to include more and more capabilities in the instruction set. In the 1980s, however, most decided that the extra complexity of large instruction sets was not worth the convenience. Most modern chips are therefore built on the principles of reduced instruction set computing or RISC.

INTEGER

A whole number, such as 1, 2 or 3, but not 1.5 or 6.54, which are real numbers but not integers. Calculations performed only with integers are referred to as integer arithmetic. (See also REAL NUMBER.)

INTEGRATED SERVICES DIGITAL NETWORK
See ISDN.

INTEL
The company which invented the MICROPROCESSOR. Unlike many SEMICONDUCTOR innovators, which have seen their innovations gain commercial glory in the hands of rivals, Intel has dominated the microprocessor sector for nearly two decades.

Intel was founded by Robert Noyce, Andy Grove and other engineers who broke away from Fairchild Semiconductor, the firm which was the grandfather of both commercial innovation in semiconductors and Silicon Valley entrepreneurialism. Its early products were mostly computer MEMORY chips, but in 1968 one of its engineers, Ted Hoff, realised that advances in the miniaturisation of circuitry enabled him to fit on to a single piece of silicon all of the components of a computer's CPU (that is, its calculating engine). Thus the microprocessor was born.

Because of the performance trade-offs in miniaturisation, Intel had to struggle to sell early microprocessors. Its first customer was a Japanese firm which used the device to build a pocket calculator. In 1980, however, IBM chose Intel's 8088 microprocessor to power its entry in the PERSONAL COMPUTER market and a *de facto* STANDARD was set. Although Intel was driven out of the mainstream memory chip business by fierce Japanese competition in the early 1980s, its microprocessors have gone from strength to strength.

Intel's microprocessors now power over 80% of the personal computers sold in the world. Its dominance is buttressed by the millions of SOFTWARE packages written to run on its microprocessors, which would have to be adapted or rewritten for any competitor who hoped to usurp Intel's role. The fifth generation of Intel microprocessors was called the PENTIUM after Intel discovered that its tradition of numbering chips (8088, 80286,

80386, 80486) rendered the names unprotectable by either copyright or trademark.

INTERFACE
The technology needed to get two computer and/or communication systems to work together. It is where things usually go wrong. In the vocabulary of open systems, engineers increasingly make a distinction between interface and IMPLEMENTATION. Interfaces are abstract, commonly agreed, public standards, available to all. Implementations turn interfaces into working programs, and are the source of proprietary competitive advantage.

INTERNATIONAL STANDARDS ORGANISATION
See ISO.

INTERNET
The world's largest computer NETWORK, which by 1997 linked over 16m computers and more than 100m people, and was still growing at 50–100% a year. The Internet has managed this growth because it is a new kind of infrastructure, built to mutually agreed technical standards, largely with private capital and effort and from the bottom up.

Nobody is in charge of the Internet; its size is measured simply by sending out a query from a computer in California and asking all machines that receive the message to reply. Its technical standards are all voluntarily, although those who do not wish to abide by them will simply not be able to communicate with their fellows. Connecting to the Internet is nearly as simple as renting a connection to somebody else on the Internet; there is a minimum of bureaucracy and administration.

Like any computer network the Internet is defined by the answers to two questions: Who talks to whom? and How do they do it? Technically, the answer to the first question concerns addresses. Each computer on the Internet is given a name (for people to use) and a number (for other machines to use). Translation between names and numbers is automatic, and the organisation of addresses reflects the overall organisation of the network.

Like street addresses, each Internet address reflects a hierarchy. To deliver a letter to St James's Street, London, the post office might first send the letter to the London sorting office and then let it find the proper street. So too with delivering E-MAIL to *jb@zeno.somewhere.uk*. To the Internet-savvy, this message denotes a person called *jb* at a machine called *zeno* in the DOMAIN *somewhere.uk*. Like paper mail, the message can first be delivered to the computer managing the *somewhere.uk* domain, and then that computer can find the machine called *zeno*.

This hierarchy of responsibilities is one of the keys to the Internet's fast growth. It makes its complexity manageable by devolving responsibility for each system to the lowest possible point. To a large extent, each of the many networks making up the Internet can hide its internal workings from the others. It is up to individual network administrators to choose how, and how much, they want the machines in their domain to participate in the larger life of the network.

At the most basic level, the Internet offers three ways for the people and machines it connects to communicate.

- **E-MAIL.** The postal system of the Internet, transmitting the text of letters and, sometimes, digital "parcels" with attached SOFTWARE programs, documents or DATA.
- **TELNET.** Using this, a person on one computer connected to the Internet can LOG ON to another computer on the Net and use its services.
- **FTP.** Transmits bulk data across the Net.

From the beginning, one of the purposes of the Internet was to support research into networking technology. So the Internet is continually evolving. The WORLD WIDE WEB made the Internet almost as easy to use as pointing and clicking on a MACINTOSH computer. In just a few years the ease and

speed with which the Web can serve up INFORMA-
TION from around the world has made it by far the
largest source of traffic over the Internet. Today,
experiments are being made in creating a more
interactive network, with videoconferencing and
the network equivalent of voice telephone calls.

For the future, the Internet faces challenges that
are technical, political and cultural. They include:

- **Quality of service.** To provide video and
  other high-BANDWIDTH services, the Internet
  needs to incorporate new technologies like
  RSVP and ATM.
- **Censorship.** Compromises need to be
  reached on how to keep pornography and
  the seamier side of the Net out of children's
  sight, without compromising the rights of
  adults to speak freely.
- **Security.** To provide a secure place for
  electronic commerce, the Internet needs to
  adopt new standards like SET.
- **Management.** Registration of a DOMAIN NAME
  and other Net-management matters need to
  be put on a more formal footing to
  correspond with the Internet's growing
  commercial importance.
- **Regulation.** Governments must sort out
  where the Net fits into broader schemes of
  telecoms regulation, including the UNIVERSAL
  SERVICE obligation.

*The Coca-Cola machine at Carnegie Mellon
University in Pittsburgh is connected to the
Internet. To find out how many cokes it holds type
finger coke@cs.cmu.edu.*

INTERNET ENGINEERING TASK FORCE
See IETF.

INTERNET PROTOCOL
The IP in TCP/IP, these are the technical standards
which specify how packets on the INTERNET are
routed from one machine to another. Each PACKET

travels independently, and packets may follow very different routes. In terms of the SEVEN LAYER REFERENCE MODEL, IP is the NETWORK layer of the Internet.

INTERNETWORKING

A generic term used to describe the process of linking together different networks – as is done, for example, in the INTERNET (and from which the Internet took its name).

INTERNET SERVICE PROVIDER

A company that provides connections to the INTERNET. Strictly, ISPs (as they are commonly known) connect users direct to the Internet, unlike ONLINE service providers, such as Compuserve and AOL, which connect through their own proprietary communications systems.

The Net interprets censorship as damage, and routes around it.
John Gilmore

INTERNET TELEPHONY

A technique for transmitting voice over the INTERNET. There are three challenges to overcome. First, and simplest, the steady stream of voice has to be reduced to the discrete packets that are transmitted over the Internet. Second, the volume of DATA has to be compressed by about three-quarters, because modems get only about one-third to one-quarter of the BANDWIDTH typically allotted to voice lines. The third and hardest problem is ensuring that the packets arrive in order and without delays, so that voice can be reconstituted without an … noying … paus … es.

COMPRESSION SOFTWARE can solve the first two problems, but achieving quality of service remains the Achilles heel. When it is solved, Internet telephony will be appealingly cheap, for FLAT-RATE PRICING schemes typically used to provide Internet services rapidly undercut USAGE-BASED PRICING schemes used on long-distance telephony. Internet telephony should make most progress on intranets, where managers have more control over quality of service. Bottlenecks and regulatory skirmishing with telephone companies determined to protect market share will limit its growth on public networks.

INTER-OPERABILITY

Like STANDARD, inter-operability is rapidly becoming a meaningless word in information technology. When technology companies talk about inter-operable systems, they imply that the systems can easily be made to work together. But there many different interpretations of what "easily" might mean in this context. *Caveat emptor.*

INTERPRETER

A piece of SOFTWARE which understands and executes programs written in high-level languages like BASIC, LISP and PROLOG. In contrast to a COMPILER, an interpreter executes the statements of these languages directly, without the initial step of translating them into MACHINE CODE. The extra effort required for on-the-fly translation means that interpreted programs run more slowly than compiled ones, but they are faster and easier to DEBUG. Languages for experimental programming, like LISP and Prolog (widely used in ARTIFICIAL INTELLIGENCE), are interpreted. Those for production systems, like C, C++ and COBOL, are compiled.

INTERRUPT

A way of handling unpredictable events within a computer, like the press of a key on a keyboard, or the arrival of a message over a NETWORK. As the name suggests, an interrupt forces the MICROPROCESSOR to drop what it is doing and deal with the new event, after which it can go back to work as normal. Interrupts are used as an alternative to POLLING, where the microprocessor continually asks the keyboard (or the network PORT, or whatever) if they have any work that needs doing. The advantage of interrupts is that they do not waste time looking for work when there is none to do; the disadvantage is the complexity and potential difficulties of making sure that, even if an interrupt occurs when least expected (as they inevitably seem to do), the computer can happily resume work as normal.

INTRANET

A NETWORK using the same TCP/IP technology as the global INTERNET, but designed primarily for use within a single organisation. Intranets are the fastest-growing area of investment in the Internet; they are also something of an illusion.

An American Express poll found that by 1997 over two-thirds of large US companies were investing in intranets. Jupiter Communications enthusiastically estimated its spending at over $10 billion. The justification for such spending is savings on network administration overheads and improved internal communications. Intranets have been used to create electronic discussion forums, simplify access to corporate databases by making them accessible via a WEB BROWSER, automate form-filling procedures like expense claims, disseminate corporate information via CASTANET and other PUSH MEDIA, and to provide easily updateable ONLINE directories of employees.

As many success stories demonstrate, Internet technologies, particularly Web browsers like NETSCAPE's Navigator and Communicator, can provide more benefits than proprietary GROUPWARE products like Lotus Notes, at a fraction of the price. The sting in the tail of intranets, though, is that having installed one to improve internal communication, most companies discover that the notion of "internal" becomes difficult to define. A FIREWALL and other security SOFTWARE can keep intranets safe from unwanted intruders, but who in this new world is unwanted? An intranet can grow rapidly into an EXTRANET as companies realise that allowing customers and suppliers access to corporate intranets can profitably improve relationships.

IO

Computer shorthand for input-output; that is, the work of getting DATA into the computer and back out again. These are by far the most time consuming and tricky jobs in computing. In part because most must interact mechanically with the real world, IO devices work more slowly than the whizzing of electrons within CPUs. So, in practice, most programs spend most of their time waiting for input or output; they are, in the vernacular, IO-bound. MULTI-TASKING operating systems were originally created to take advantage of these delays, by allowing another program to use the CPU while its predecessor waited for IO and then reverting to the original program when IO finished.

IP
See INTERNET PROTOCOL.

ISA
Short for Industry Standard Architecture, the BUS used to link the MICROPROCESSOR and other HARDWARE of IBM's original PERSONAL COMPUTER. Although widely copied, it is now rivalled by faster, more powerful PCI, EISA and MCA buses.

ISDN
Abbreviation for Integrated Services Digital Network, the next generation of higher-BANDWIDTH, DIGITAL communications services. Not only is ISDN a digital service, which offers better error correction than today's ANALOGUE telephone services, but it also offers at least twice the bandwidth of existing analogue services. The key difference between ISDN and plain old telephone service (POTS) is that it accepts that, in the modern world, voices will share the line with other services.

ISO
The International Standards Organisation, a STANDARD-setting body which has created the SEVEN LAYER REFERENCE MODEL, a widely used way of categorising different sorts of communications capabilities, among other standards.

ISP
See INTERNET SERVICE PROVIDER.

JANET

Acronym for Joint Academic Network, the UK's version of the USA's INTERNET. A recent, higher-BANDWIDTH version of JANET is called SuperJANET.

JAVA

A programming language designed for use on the INTERNET. Created by SUN MICROSYSTEMS, Java is the first popular language to take it for granted that the computers it runs on will be seamlessly linked over networks. So Java was built to new design criteria. Its priorities include the following.

- **Portability.** Any Java program can run on any computer, regardless of OPERATING SYSTEM or MICROPROCESSOR. Instead of manipulating the computer directly, Java programs run on a "virtual machine", often built into a WEB BROWSER, which shields them from the incompatibilities which plague other programs.
- **Security.** The Java virtual machine limits the ability of any Java program to do damage to the underlying computer; for example, by deleting files. So it is impossible to write viruses or other harmful SOFTWARE in Java.
- **Modularity.** Java takes full advantage of the capabilities of OBJECT ORIENTED software to divide functions into discrete components, called JAVA BEANS, each of which can be downloaded separately. Starting with a basic program that does not hog MEMORY or DISK space, users can quickly and easily upgrade it with exactly the extra functions they need.

Owing in part to its success in meeting these criteria, use of Java has grown like wildfire. At first, Java was used mostly on the WORLD WIDE WEB, to create animations and other adornments for Web sites. But by 1997 some software companies were launching mainstream applications, such as word processors and spreadsheets programmed in Java.

JAVA BEANS

SOFTWARE components created in JAVA. Each bean provides a specific function; for example, a mini-SPREADSHEET for manipulating numbers, or a tax and postage calculator for the corporate shipping department. Because they were designed to be downloaded on the fly, Java beans are different from WIDGET, VISUAL BASIC control and other more traditional software components in a subtle but important way. For traditional components, it is the programmer's responsibility to make sure that the component will work with whatever software should call upon it. Java beans, by contrast, can engage in a sort of negotiation, albeit a very rudimentary one, with other software to see if they can indeed provide the capabilities required by the other program.

JAVASCRIPT

Not to be confused with JAVA, Javascript is a programming language designed to make Web pages more interactive. As a language, Javascript is based on C++, but its claim to fame is the ease with which it enables a programmer to access and manipulate the contents of a Web page. So an interactive form, for example, can use Javascript to check that the information entered into its blanks is both complete and sensible before sending it off down the NETWORK for processing.

JCL

Short for Job Control Language, a programming language used in IBM mainframes and notorious for its awkwardness and insistence on obscure points of SYNTAX. Most languages will, for example, happily allow two or more spaces where they expected one, but JCL insists that one and only one is right; anything else is unacceptable.

JOB

As in normal usage, a task for a computer to do.

JOIN

The fundamental technique for relating fragments

of DATA stored in a RELATIONAL DATABASE. Relational databases store information in tables, and, to ease management, designers try to keep tables small and simple. So how do you ask a complicated question? With a join.

Say a computer shopkeeper had a database containing one table with the names and addresses of customers, and another with a record of what each customer bought, indexed by name. To send a mailing to all of those who have bought Brand X computers, the shopkeeper must do a join on the two tables to associate the addresses of Brand X buyers with the information about their computing preferences. To be joined, tables must obviously share an index (in this case, the name of the customer). Then it is relatively straightforward to marry up the information in one to that of the other.

JPEG

Joint Picture Experts Group, referring to standards for the COMPRESSION and format of DIGITAL images. JPEG files are pictures stored digitally in the JPEG format. MPEG is roughly the same, but for moving pictures.

K

An abbreviation for KILO, as in 256k MEMORY chip.

KERBEROS

A set of protocols developed at the Massachusetts Institute of Technology to maintain security in distributed systems. Kerberos ensures that users can gain access to only those files and services to which they have been granted access by the systems administrator. In a distributed computing environment, where users move from machine to machine and new services are regularly being added, this is a lot harder than it sounds.

KERMIT

A communications program often used to send DATA between personal computers and larger machines. It comes with its own, eponymous PROTOCOL for detecting and correcting errors. Both program and protocol were developed at Columbia University and named after the frog on *Sesame Street*, a children's television programme.

KERNEL

The heart of a MULTI-TASKING OPERATING SYSTEM. One of the key design challenges in creating an operating system that will allow several users to share the same machine is to make sure that one program cannot mess up another's work, even if that program was created by a user who maliciously wishes to do so. This requires a benevolent dictator to manage all of the programs working on the machine: sharing out time on the CPU, making sure that two programs do not try to use the PRINTER at the same time, and so on. That benevolent dictator is the kernel.

A trend in operating systems has been to reduce the size of the kernel (to create micro-kernels) by building into the kernel only a few, but very powerful functions. Programs do not interact with the micro-kernel directly, but through an intermediary. The hope is that by building clever intermediaries, systems developers might enable operating systems to take on different personalities, with the same underlying micro-kernel appearing through one intermediary as, say, IBM's OS/2 operating system and through another as UNIX.

KEY

The information used to decode an encrypted message. For best practice see PUBLIC-KEY CRYPTO-GRAPHY.

KEYWORD

A word used as a tag or marker for INFORMATION RETRIEVAL. Keywords say what a book, article or other piece of text is about. They are typically abstracted by professional librarians, who read the text and then annotate it with the words they think best describe its content. It is then easy to use a computer to search for articles whose keywords match the subjects of interest to some inquiring mind. The problem with keywords, however, is the difficulty of maintaining consistency and accuracy when different articles are read, classified and searched for by different librarians. One librarian's "information technology" maybe another's "computer science".

KEY ESCROW

A scheme proposed by security agencies that would make PUBLIC-KEY CRYPTOGRAPHY more easily wiretapped. Although the details differ, anyone using public-key cryptography would have to deposit a copy of their PRIVATE KEY with an agency designated by the government. Should police or other security forces wish to listen in on encrypted conversations, that agency would be obliged hand over the private keys.

KEY RECOVERY

A scheme to reconstitute lost keys to encrypted material. Some schemes involve the straightforward ploy of storing a copy of the key in a safe place. More ambitious schemes allow keys to be recovered using advanced mathematics – almost like breaking the code.

K

KILL
To stop a program from running. Most operating systems provide kill commands which can be typed at the keyboard to stop unwanted programs, even if some BUG has stopped the program from responding to its usual command to quit.

KILL FILE
A way of filtering out annoying messages from a USENET NEWS GROUP and other electronic forums. Even in an otherwise interesting subject, some people and/or topics can become so annoying that you never want to see them again. Kill files offer a way of making sure that you don't. By entering a name, subject or other distinguishing feature of the unwanted messages into the kill file, SOFTWARE can automatically delete the potentially offending messages before they are read. Ignorance is then bliss.

KILO
Strictly, the prefix denotes a thousand, but as the computer world counts in twos rather than tens it is here used to refer to $1,024$ (2^{10}).

KLUGE
Pronounced *klooj*, from the German for clever; a too-clever programming trick. Like a HACK, but generally used with an element of disdain to denote work that is either an obviously temporary fix or else over-elaborate.

Where is the knowledge that is lost in information? Where is the wisdom that is lost in knowledge?
T. S. Eliot

KNOWLEDGE ENGINEERING
The process of extracting the knowledge of a human expert for use in building a computerised EXPERT SYSTEM.

LAMBDA CALCULUS

A theory of calculation created by a mathematician, Alonzo Church. The lambda calculus enables mathematicians to prove results about what can and cannot be calculated. It also provided inspiration for the programming language LISP.

LAN

See LOCAL AREA NETWORK.

LANGUAGE UNDERSTANDING

There are two parts to the task of teaching a computer to talk. The first is to recognise words, and the second is to understand them. When words are written, recognising words is easy. But speech requires more effort.

Linguists have long known that all words are composed of a handful of basic sounds, called phonemes, strung together in different combinations. In theory, then, recognising a spoken word should be little harder than recognising a written one; just keep track of the sequence of phonemes. The snag, however, is that various phonemes sound different in different contexts. The same phoneme can be pronounced differently by different people. The same person can pronounce them differently depending on whether he is asking a question or making a statement. Worst of all, people often do not pause between words as meticulously as they put spaces in sentences.

So recognising spoken language requires statistical models which make educated guesses about which words and phonemes they might be hearing, and constantly refine those guesses as each new sound is heard. Given training to accustom them to the voice of a particular speaker, some such systems can take dictation consisting of thousands of different words. But if they must cope with any speaker, performance falls dramatically. AT&T has been experimenting with replacing some of its long-distance telephone operators with a system that can understand the ten digits, yes, no, and little else.

Given words, the harder task is to make sense

of them. The problem is mostly the sheer amount of knowledge required to disentangle even a seemingly simple sentence. For example, the sentence "The turkeys are ready to eat" has two entirely different meanings – one for the Christmas table and one for the barnyard. To distinguish one from the other requires more than just the meanings of the words; it also requires a lot of the common-sense knowledge that people take for granted, but which computers lack utterly. Although computers are beginning to do simple things with language, like routing incoming telexes at banks, real understanding is a long way off.

LASER PRINTER
A PRINTER which creates high-quality, near-typeset printing by using a laser beam to etch characters. The laser beam creates small changes in the electrical field on a large, smooth drum. Where the beam has changed the field, toner sticks to the drum, which is then heated and pressed on to paper to print.

LAST IN, FIRST OUT
See LIFO.

LDAP
Short for Lightweight Directory Access Protocol, a PROTOCOL designed to make it easier to look up names and addresses over computer networks. Adopted by the IETF as a standard, LDAP was designed to work with existing address-book standards, like X.500, and to make them more useful by papering over their incompatibilities.

LEASED LINE
A way of buying bulk telecommunications BANDWIDTH. Instead of paying the NETWORK provider by the minute, a leased line provides some fixed amount of capacity for a flat annual fee, which must be paid whether the line is used or not. Leasing capacity is in most countries more economic for firms that transmit lots of DATA, but costs vary widely from country to country.

LED
See LIGHT-EMITTING DIODE.

LEGACY SYSTEM
An ageing computer system, usually on a MAIN-FRAME, often one which inhibits corporate change. In many companies legacy systems dominate the IT-management agenda. They are generally difficult to modify and to replace. They are written in programming languages never encountered by programmers under the age of 40, and years of haphazard modification have made the code both obscure and fragile. Even seemingly innocuous changes can break the program. Yet legacy systems often perform crucial corporate functions, like accounts receivable or inventory management.

IT managers have developed several different approaches to updating legacy systems.

- **Scrap them.** Some systems are simply so old and flaky that there is no alternative but to rebuild them from scratch.
- **Wrap them.** Some legacy systems work perfectly well, but they employ technologies that work awkwardly with modern networks and CLIENT-SERVER systems, so companies are building wrappers which can intermediate between old and new. So-called hub SOFTWARE enables old legacy systems to communicate over modern networks, and it can seamlessly gather together DATA scattered across several databases to answer a single query (which is useful in the modern managerial pursuit of building cross-functional processes). Another technology, called object wrappers, can enable legacy systems, or components of legacy systems, to work with modern OBJECT-ORIENTED software.
- **Convert them.** Software exists, particularly for ageing databases, that can take data from an outdated DATABASE and recast it in the format required by a new RELATIONAL DATABASE.

The really hard question for managers to ask themselves, however, is how to prevent today's new systems from becoming tomorrow's legacies. Depressingly, that is a question with more good ideas than solid answers.

LIFO
Last In, First Out, an approach to managing incoming and outgoing DATA. LIFO dictates that the most recently arrived piece of data will be the next to be used. Although this changes the order of the data in ways that depend somewhat unpredictably on the timing of arrivals and departures, it turns out to be convenient for many computing applications. A commonly used form of LIFO BUFFER is called a STACK.

LIGHT-EMITTING DIODE
A diode that glows when a current is passed through it. Light-emitting diodes (LEDs) are typically used in circuits to show if a piece of machinery, such as a DISK drive, is on or off.

LIGHTWEIGHT DIRECTORY ACCESS PROTOCOL
See LDAP.

LINEAR PROGRAMMING
Describes computer programs concerned with minimisation or maximisation. As the name suggests, linear programming techniques can cope only with formulae which describe linear costs, values or whatever; that is, whose values per unit are constant. (The cost of a telephone call, for example, is linear because, typically, calls are charged at so much per minute – so the total cost of any call is simply a multiple of the per-minute charge.) With the constraint that the values involved be linear, and powerful computers, linear programming methods can find the highest-value, lowest-cost or otherwise best way of approaching problems described even by large collections of formulae. The most commonly used form of linear programming is called the SIMPLEX ALGORITHM.

LINK

A connection between two items of HYPERTEXT. In some hypertext systems links can be labelled to make explicit the relationship they denote. So one link might be labelled "supporting argument" and another "contrary argument". In theory, labels make it easier to solve the perennial problem of hypertext links, which is maintaining a sense of direction in the sea of INFORMATION. In practice, adding more information (on the labels) to all that is already there can easily be mishandled to create more confusion.

LINKER

A piece of SOFTWARE which assembles the components of a program for execution. Programs are typically written as a collection of subroutines, each of which does a specific task. In order to execute a SUBROUTINE, however, the computer must know where it is located in MEMORY. This is usually not known when the program is translated into MACHINE CODE during compilation; so the COMPILER leaves markers wherever it needs to call a subroutine, labelled, in effect, "wherever subroutine X may be". The linker then fills in the blanks.

LISP

An acronym derived from List Processing, a FUNCTIONAL PROGRAMMING language created by John McCarthy, a computer scientist at Stanford University, and widely used in ARTIFICIAL INTELLIGENCE. True to its name, LISP – and the functional programming traditions of the LAMBDA CALCULUS which inspired it – views the world in terms of lists and functions. This turns out to be remarkably convenient, once you get the hang of it.

LOCAL AREA NETWORK

A DATA NETWORK that links nearby computers, often in the same room, or at least in the same building. The most common local area networks (LANs) are ETHERNET and TOKEN RING. On the horizon, however, are faster networks based on fibre optics, including FDDI.

LOCAL LOOP

Strictly, the link between a customer's telephone (or fax machine, or MODEM, or whatever) and the nearest telephone switch. In practice, the term is loosely used to refer to the business of providing communications service to the end user. One of the interesting developments of coming years will be the growth of competition in the local loop, and the choices people will have to make about how to communicate with their peers.

Indeed, regulators permitting, tomorrow's homes and businesses could choose between as many as five different networks, each striving to serve them.

- **POTS** (plain old telephone service). Instead of today's low BANDWIDTH telephone service, tomorrow's telephone companies will provide at least ISDN, and perhaps even higher bandwidth voice and DATA services.
- **Cable television.** In some parts of both the UK and the USA, cable television companies are offering telephone service as well as entertainment. Having laid the cables to carry television, there is little additional cost in adding telephone service over the same infrastructure.
- **Electric utilities.** With electric wires to every home and office, electric utilities already have the rights of way needed to offer telephone service. They would have to install extra equipment, but the cost of this equipment could be at least partially covered by the savings that more communication could bring in the utilities' own operations.
- **PERSONAL COMMUNICATIONS NETWORK.** In theory, new technology could enable the creation of low-cost cellular networks which offer a bandwidth somewhat greater than today's telephone services (although somewhat less than tomorrow's) at highly competitive costs. Better still, being wireless, they would also be mobile; the telephone

would live in your pocket, not on your desk.
- **Fixed cellular.** Perhaps using bandwidth freed when today's ANALOGUE television broadcasters shrink their signals into an efficiently compressed DIGITAL form, a second group of wireless communications companies may compete directly with wire-based services by offering radio-based communications via a transceiver attached to the side of the building. It would not be mobile, but it could be cheap.

The introduction of competition into the local loop presents a difficult problem for regulators. Having witnessed how competition has reduced costs while boosting quality in long-distance communications, many countries now wish to unleash potential competition in the local loop. But it is more difficult to ensure that competition is fair, and that incumbent companies do not make it hard for their competitors to woo potential customers. Many regulators are also worried about the impact of competition on UNIVERSAL SERVICE.

Rate regulation has in the past forced telephone companies to provide residential telephone service at a loss. Although there is surprisingly little hard evidence about the size of this loss (or whether there still need be a loss given modern technology and proper accounting procedures) most regulators assume that they will need to find some way to continue to subsidise residential telephone rates even as they introduce competition, lest people find the price of communications moving beyond their reach as its importance for their well-being increases. Given that competition and subsidies coexist uneasily, universal service augments the regulators' challenge.

LOCK
A way of preventing conflict between two programs which might otherwise simultaneously try to use the same FILE, PRINTER or other resource. Before using the resource, programs check to see if some other program has "locked" access to it,

which is often done by creating a specially named file on the DISK.

LOG ON

To begin using a computer, a process which usually requires entering your name and PASSWORD at the keyboard. Hence "log-on prompt", which is what appears on the computer display after you have successfully logged on. Log in is of course the same thing with different words.

LOGIC

A formal method of reasoning. Informally, the term is used to describe choices and calculations made by a program, or to distinguish circuits which calculate, like a MICROPROCESSOR, from those which merely regurgitate, like MEMORY. More strictly, logic describes a mathematical system of DEDUCTION, which uses strict rules of reasoning to determine the truth or falsity of statements.

Many of the rules of deduction of formal logic are built into the connectives: and, or, not, and so on. For example, the statement "A and B" is true if and only if the statement A is true and the statement B is true; while "A or B" is true if either is true, and "not A" is true if and only if A is false. So "Lucy is a girl and Lucy is a boy" is necessarily false (for people, at least), while "Lucy is a girl or Lucy is a boy" is necessarily true.

Similar rules apply to logic circuits on chips. An AND circuit is on if all of its inputs are on; an OR circuit is on if one or more of its inputs is on; and so on.

Leaving circuits aside, formal, mathematically rigorous logic comes in several forms. Some of the most commonly used are as follows.

- **Propositional logic.** The simplest useful logic, propositional logic talks about the truth or falsity of statements using and, or, not, and so on.
- **First-order logic.** To the basic capabilities of propositional logic, first-order logic adds the ability to talk about variables, that is

things whose identity is not known in advance. Such variables can be universally quantified, which is to say that everything that that variable might stand for must have some property (say, be red in colour). Or they can be existentially quantified, which is to say that there must exist something which that variable stands for, and which has the given property.

- **Modal logic.** While most logic talks about things that are once and forever true or false – that circles are round, for example – modal logic provides extra mechanisms for reasoning about things that might change, for example the idea that Caesar is dead (for he wasn't always so).

Logic: the art of thinking and reasoning in strict accordance with the limitations and incapacities of the human understanding.
Ambrose Bierce, *The Devil's Dictionary*

LOGIC PROGRAMMING

Describes a family of DECLARATIVE PROGRAMMING languages which compute using rules very similar to LOGIC. Probably the most popular logic programming language is Prolog, created by Alain Colmerauer at the University of Marseille and Robert Kowalski, then at the University of Edinburgh, now at Imperial College, London.

Their insight was that the rules of logic specified a kind of programming language. Given statements of the form "X is a mammal if X is a dog" and "Y is warm-blooded if Y is a mammal", and a DATABASE naming several particular dogs, a computer could automatically deduce various facts about their blood temperature. (More rules make a program more useful.) Better still, it could do so without forcing the programmer to specify in tedious detail how the DEDUCTION was to be managed. So, in theory at least, programs could be written by specifying facts and logical rules of deduction, not machine mumbo-jumbo. The snag with this vision, however, is that some rules of deduction are easier for the computer to manage than others. Thus in practice the programmer cannot actually ignore the underlying technical details of how the language works without risking unpleasant surprises.

LOOP

One of the most commonly used constructs in computer programming, a loop is a series of instructions that repeats until some condition is met: perhaps all the characters in a FILE have been processed, or the loop has been repeated 100 times. A common programming error is to write a loop whose exit condition will never be met, in which case the loop will repeat endlessly until the program is killed. This is called an infinite loop. Not coincidentally, the street on which is located the headquarters of APPLE Computer is called Infinite Loop. But none of the programmers seem to mind having an address named after a mistake.

LZW ALGORITHM

The Lempel-Zev-Welch ALGORITHM is one of the most effective techniques for DATA COMPRESSION. It builds up a dictionary of sequences of characters with each entry numbered. When a previously encountered sequence is met again the number is substituted for the characters. The cleverness lies in the algorithm doing this coding so that the receiving program can decode and decompress the data as easily as the encoding one can compress it.

M
An abbreviation for MEGA, as in 64M MEMORY chip.

MACHINE CODE
A synonym for ASSEMBLY LANGUAGE.

MACHINE LEARNING
The process of teaching a computer new tricks. To some extent, machines can be taught more or less like people: by showing them examples of what is right and what is wrong and allowing them to compare. But computers are much stupider than people, and in particular they have little idea of what concepts might be relevant to a specific problem. So a perennial struggle for those who would teach computers is to focus the machine's attention on the specific features of a problem that differentiate a right example from a wrong one. A square is not different from a circle because you only see one when it is dark outside, although a computer which had only seen circles at night would be quite happy to believe so.

One way of overcoming this problem is to construct carefully the examples used in teaching, so that each differs from the others by only one or two significant features. Another way for computers to learn is for them to try to fit each example into a set of ready-made templates, or explanations, with a human to correct them when the explanations go wrong. Yet another way is for the machine simply to serve as a memory aide, indexing all of the situations it has encountered so that a person can more easily retrieve the experience of situations similar to the one at hand (see CASE-BASED REASONING). Finally, both the GENETIC ALGORITHM and the NEURAL NET in some sense learn by adapting to their environment.

MACINTOSH
APPLE's flagship computer, the Macintosh revolutionised computing by bringing the easy-to-use, graphical user interface (GUI) to the desktop, popularising ideas developed at Xerox's Palo Alto Research Center. The Macintosh was the first

popular computer sold with a MOUSE; it was the first to use a MENU-DRIVEN INTERFACE; and it was the first to mix text and graphics indiscriminately on the screen. Yet despite all of these breakthroughs Macintosh languishes in a niche in computer markets. Ultimately, Macintosh was brought low by the arrogance of its designers. Having designed an "insanely great" computer, Apple assumed first that people would pay a price premium for the machine, and second that they would appreciate that the Macintosh way of doing things was the one true way. Neither was true, at least not to the extent Macintosh designers believed. By the time Apple learned humility, many of its distinctive features had been replicated by others, notably MICROSOFT's WINDOWS.

> *If the automobile had followed the same development as the computer, a Rolls-Royce would today cost $100, get a million miles per gallon, and explode once a year killing everyone inside.*
> Robert X. Cringely

MACRO PROGRAMMING

Macros, as statements in macro-programming languages are called, are a simple form of programming which serve as a boon to those who hate to type. They come in two basic flavours. In an APPLICATION program (such as a SPREADSHEET), macros are a way of automating commonly performed sequences of operations. For example, an accountant reformatting a column of numbers time and again for a weekly report might wish to create an automated procedure to do the job with a single command. Some spreadsheets will help to write just such a macro by recording the usual sequence of key strokes to be stored as a new macro.

In programming languages macros achieve similar ends but by different means. Should programmers find themselves frequently repeating some long series of statements with a few variations, many languages allow them to write a macro which will enable them to type just the name of the macro, and from that recreate the whole set of statements. Because both sorts of macros hide what they are doing beneath a layer of convenience, they can make programs obscure and difficult for anybody other than the person who wrote the macro to work with. But they are useful.

MAE

Short for Metropolitan Area Ethernet, MAEs have become the place where the networks that make up the INTERNET join together to exchange DATA. The two oldest and largest are MAE East (in Reston, Virginia) and MAE West (in San José, California). Instead of trying to connect all the networks to a single switch, it proved easier simply to link them via a high-speed central NETWORK, which allows packets to zip from one to the next.

A seat on the network, though, does not guarantee that the others on the network will in fact carry your data. Deciding which networks will exchange packets with others is the subject of a set of complex and extremely ad hoc agreements for PEERING. Needless to say, peering arrangements are one of the most hard-argued and contentious areas of business on the Internet.

MAILING LIST

Mailing lists take advantage of the ease with which E-MAIL can be duplicated to create privately organised discussion groups. E-mail sent to a central mailbox is automatically duplicated and sent to everyone on the list, which may contain thousands of names. Not surprisingly, mailing lists have sprung up across the INTERNET like mushrooms on an autumn morning – both private and open to all – to discuss just about anything.

MAINFRAME

The kind of big computer that needs its own air-conditioned room and attendants to cater to its obscure whims. Mainframes are widely considered to be outdated dinosaurs, yet many corporations rely on them for the basic, and crucial, operations of accounting, payroll, and the like.

The problem is that the machines were designed under very different assumptions about computer capabilities and economics than exist today.

Early mainframes cost $1m or so when that was a lot of money. The technology was young, cantankerous and unreliable. As it cost a large multiple of the annual salaries of those who would be employed to tend it, it made sense to throw a lot of time and people at managing the reliability and performance of the machine. Today, by contrast, a high-powered PERSONAL COMPUTER costs less than a month's salary for the programmers who make them work, and computing economics has been stood on its head.

The advantages and disadvantages of mainframes today are still largely determined by decisions made when the old economics still applied. Given proper management they can be rock-solid reliable. But they are expensive to buy and to run, at least as measured by cost per unit of computing horsepower, and developing new programs for them is relatively slow and cumbersome.

IBM introduced its first mainframe computer, the 701, in 1952.

MASTER-SLAVE
Describes a relationship between two computers of the same sort as that applying to people of the same name. One tells the other what to do and when to do it – with no ifs, ands or buts. This is in contrast to a CLIENT-SERVER relationship, in which one machine is making requests of the other that may, in theory at least, be deferred.

MATERIALS REQUIREMENTS PLANNING
See MRP.

MATRIX
A name for CYBERSPACE coined by William Gibson in the novel *Neuromancer*. It is also a mathematical technique widely used in computer graphics and neural nets, where several different equations

must be applied simultaneously.

MATRIX PRINTER

A type of computer PRINTER which forms characters using a rectangular matrix of fine needles. To form, for example, the letter a, the print-head strikes the ribbon with only those needles which will form the shape of the letter. Although matrix printers are getting better, the marks of individual needles can still typically be seen in the resulting image which gives it a dotty, computerish look.

MEETING SUPPORT SYSTEMS

SOFTWARE and other tools designed to enable a group of people to work together more productively. In theory, at least, computers can help people both to share information and to reach consensus. But taking advantage of these abilities can be tricky.

Experience has shown that people will speak more freely over E-MAIL than face to face. So electronic discussions are useful for overcoming social barriers that might otherwise hinder brainstorming. Similarly, computers can provide everybody in a meeting with a record of what has been said, or reach into remote databases for relevant facts.

Often the hardest part of using computers productively in a meeting, however, is to shift from sharing information to building consensus. Computers can be used for anonymous voting on issues of interest. But it is often hard to create electronically the emotional commitment from which true consensus is built. So many meeting-support systems employ a trained facilitator to work alongside the machines, thus leaving information to the machines and emotions to the humans.

MEGA-

Strictly, a prefix denoting 1 million, but as the computer world counts in twos instead of tens, it here means 1,048,576 (the nearest power of two).

MEMORY

Where DATA and programs are stored on a computer. Computer memory comes in two basic forms. Main memory sits inside the machine, and holds data on SEMICONDUCTOR memory chips. Computers that run a variety of different programs use RAM, or, more specifically, DRAM. Appliances and computer games, which simply repeat the same programs over and over again, use ROM. Retrieval from main memory is quick, in the order of a few billionths of a second. But main memory is expensive and often impermanent. Any information stored in RAM disappears when the power is turned off.

Secondary memory includes disks, tape and other more permanent media. These are slower: the fastest serve up data within thousandths of a second and some take even longer. But they are cheap and they store data for years, even with the power switched off. At least most of the time they store data for years (see also CRASH and BACK-UP).

MENU
Key component of a MENU-DRIVEN INTERFACE.

MENU-DRIVEN INTERFACE
A computer INTERFACE which allows users to choose commands from a menu of alternatives that pops up on the screen. This is an easier-to-use but less flexible alternative to a COMMAND-LINE INTERFACE, which requires users to type commands on to a blank screen (and thus also requires them to remember what all the commands are).

METHODOLOGY
A discipline for designing and building computer systems. The heart of a methodology is a way of analysing business systems, and representing that analysis in a form that can, in turn, be turned into working computer programs. The hope is that a disciplined approach will yield better results.

There is no shortage of methodologies to choose from. Nearly all IT departments and consultants have their own, each with advantages and disadvantages. But all methodologies suffer from a generic limitation. As IT projects become larger, even well-constructed systems increasingly risk being irrelevant by the time they are completed. Discipline takes time, and the underlying business and its markets will seldom sit still for an IT project that stretches over four or five years.

More importantly, the disciplines of most methodologies require people to predict at the start how they will use their computers four or five years hence. Few can imagine just how radically computers can change their lives and the way they do business. So the discipline of methodologies has a nasty habit of locking companies into the status quo. For this reason, many companies are turning from the WATERFALL MODEL of systems development assumed by most methodologies to a SPIRAL MODEL, which is based on rapidly building a prototype of a new system and then steadily improving upon it.

METROPOLITAN AREA ETHERNET
See MAE.

MICROCOMPUTER
Another name for a PERSONAL COMPUTER. A computer powered by its own MICROPROCESSOR which, unlike a MINICOMPUTER, is typically designed to serve only one person at a time.

The MITS Altair, launched in 1975, was the first microcomputer. It cost $350 and had to be soldered together by its proud owner.

MICROPROCESSOR
A CPU which has been constructed on a single piece of silicon. Elements of a microprocessor include the following.

- **ALU** (arithmetic logic unit), which does basic calculations.
- **FPU** (floating-point unit), which does more advanced calculations involving FLOATING-POINT ARITHMETIC.
- **CACHE**, which is a local BUFFER to hold

MACHINE CODE soon to be executed and DATA soon to be worked on, for faster access than can be achieved from MEMORY.
- **REGISTER**, which is a kind of electronic workbench to hold the data being operated on by current instructions.

Bill Gates dropped out of Harvard in 1975 to write a version of the BASIC programming language for the MITS Altair after seeing it featured on the cover of Popular Electronics. Thus Microsoft was born.

MICROSOFT

Founded by a teenage programming whiz-kid, Bill Gates, in 1976, Microsoft had by the 1990s become the most powerful company in the computer world. Microsoft owes its strength to its dominance in the field of operating systems for personal computers, and it owes that, in turn, to IBM.

In 1980 Bill Gates made his living selling a version of the BASIC programming language for personal computers. IBM was rushing to create a PERSONAL COMPUTER to compete with APPLE when it approached Mr Gates to licence his programming languages. Almost as an afterthought, it also asked him for an OPERATING SYSTEM. He quickly bought the rights to a basic operating system from Seattle Computer Products, a nearby firm, improved it and renamed it DOS. Thus an empire was born.

A deeply determined businessman, Mr Gates steadily added a variety of other products to his range: WORD PROCESSOR, SPREADSHEET, other programming languages, and so on. Microsoft's hallmark was determination. Some of its products were not well received on their first release, or even their second. But in any product category which he deemed strategically important, Mr Gates simply kept trying until he got it right. To its credit, Microsoft usually did get it right in the end, and both its word processing and its spreadsheet SOFTWARE wrested dominance of their market sectors from established competitors.

Probably the most important of Microsoft's long-term bets was WINDOWS, a program which provides an easy-to-use GUI for IBM-COMPATIBLE computers. The first two releases of Windows went nowhere, but the third took off like a sky-rocket. Millions of copies are sold each month, giving Microsoft the key to its market power: control of the INTERFACE between man and computer, and between application programs (like word processors) and the underlying computer.

Microsoft is now trying to adapt Windows for all sorts of other computing devices, including smart cellular telephones, MULTI-TASKING computers and the set-top box which controls cable television. Perhaps more importantly, in 1996 Microsoft was converted to the INTERNET, and is now busily incorporating Internet technology into both its business and its technology.

Originally, Microsoft had reckoned that it would need to build its own proprietary network to bring people ONLINE. But as Microsoft Network was nearing launch, the company realised that the Internet could do everything Microsoft Network could do better and more cheaply. So Microsoft Network was reoriented towards becoming an INTERNET SERVICE PROVIDER, and its parent turned its attentions to creating content for the Internet, in effect becoming a media company.

MICROWAVE
A high-FREQUENCY electromagnetic signal often used for communications.

MIDI
Short for Musical Instrument Digital Interface, a STANDARD for exchanging DATA between a computer and a music synthesiser.

MILNET
The portion of the INTERNET used and financed by the US military.

MIMD
Short for Multiple Instructions, Multiple Data, a

form of PARALLEL PROCESSING in which each processor can execute a different instruction on different DATA. This is in contrast to SIMD (Single Instruction, Multiple Data), where each processor executes the same instruction at the same time. SIMD is like a row of reapers, swishing their scythes in unison as they move across a field of wheat. MIMD is more like the division of labour within a mill, where one person bags ground flour while another turns the mill-stone, while yet another prepares grain. As you would expect, each approach is suited to different problems.

MIME

Abbreviation for Multipurpose Internet Mailing Extensions, a way of sending MULTIMEDIA – sound, pictures, formatted text or whatever – over the INTERNET via SMTP mailing protocols, which were originally designed to handle only ASCII text.

MINICOMPUTER

An intermediate-sized computer, typically capable of serving tens of users rather than the hundreds that a MAINFRAME serves and the one served by a PERSONAL COMPUTER. In the 1970s minicomputers were the hottest thing around because they made it possible to apply computers to tasks otherwise too small to automate. By the early 1990s, however, markets for minicomputers were vanishing following the advent of CLIENT-SERVER computing. In effect, client-server split the work of the minicomputer in two. Tasks done directly for users, like word processing, had been handed over to near-ubiquitous personal computers. Meanwhile, databases – and other INFORMATION-sharing and management tasks – were being performed by specialised FILE SERVER and NETWORK machines, often a UNIX WORKSTATION.

MIPS

Millions of Instructions Per Second, a measure of the speed of a computer. MIPS is the number of assembly-language statements that a given machine executes in an average second. The problem with

MIPS, however, is that all instructions are not alike. Some chips do a lot more work with each instruction than others, so simple counts of instructions executed do not necessarily reflect accurately the amount of computing work done.

One way around this problem is to try statistically to compensate by creating an artificial, standardised instruction that reflects differences in the amount of work. So-called VAX MIPS, based on the performance of DEC's VAX computers, are often used for this purpose. Another way round the problem would be to use an alternative measure of performance. But computer-makers cannot agree on what the fairest and best alternative might be. (The best way to measure performance is to put your favourite program on the machine and see how quickly it goes for you.)

MNP-4
An error-correction PROTOCOL for a MODEM.

MNP-5
The same as MNP-4, but it also compresses DATA.

MODEM
Acronym for Modulator-Demodulator, a device that translates a stream of DIGITAL DATA into a staccato series of bleeps and bloops that can be sent over a telephone line, or some other ANALOGUE communications channel. More specifically, it is a device that does, and undoes, MODULATION.

MODERATED
Describes a NEWS GROUP or MAILING LIST in which the flow of contributions is controlled by an editor, or moderator. Instead of simply passing along all messages, as most news groups do, the moderator tries to cut the flow of information down to manageable size by weeding out those judged unworthy of a general readership.

MODULARITY
In reference to SOFTWARE, modularity describes the extent to which a program can be broken down

into discrete, independently functioning components. One of the lessons that programmers learned the hard way is that it is easy to construct programs in which everything effectively depends on everything else, and hard to live with them. Any change or modification in the SPAGHETTI CODE of a program with insufficient modularity can cause a breakdown in a seemingly unrelated part of the program. In the 1970s, however, disciplines of so-called STRUCTURED PROGRAMMING were created to help programmers to divide programs into smaller, more manageable component modules.

MODULATION

The act of encoding information into a CARRIER wave by altering its AMPLITUDE, PHASE, or FREQUENCY. Normally the carrier wave is of constant amplitude, frequency and phase. By changing one or more of these attributes in predetermined ways, a MODEM can use modulation to send information across a communications channel.

MODULO

A mathematical operation related to division, except that instead of returning the dividend it returns the remainder. Thus 14 divided by 4 is 3, but 14 modulo 4 is 2.

MONITOR

A computer screen. (See COMPOSITE MONITOR and RGB MONITOR.)

MOO

Short for MUD OBJECT ORIENTED. A MOO is a MUD (multi-user dungeon) with a programming language built in, so that, instead of just wandering around an imaginary world inside the machine, its users can shape the world to their own whims. A MOO is a kind of consensual hallucination, the nearest computer scientists have yet managed to approach the vision of the MATRIX created by the science fiction writer, William Gibson.

So far MOOs are mostly for fun. The Cyberion City MOO, hosted by a computer at MIT, allows its users to create a world within a future space station. Other MOOs involve magic and sorcery; yet others are populated by people who like to fantasise that they are small furry animals which, untrue to character, seem to spend a lot of time in a hot tub talking about their feelings.

The programming language built into MOOs gives their users great freedom to shape both their characters and the world around them. In a MUD, both the objects in the world and the actions that can be performed with them are created in advance, by the original programmers. In a MOO, users can create their own objects and actions. If someone is dissatisfied with the fire-breathing dragons supplied by the original programmers, they can create dragons with curry-breath, fire-breathing mice, or whatever.

The result of this freedom has been an outpouring of both creativity and just plain messing around. People can create their own characters in a MOO, and many use the opportunity to try out a new personality. Some become flamboyant; some change sex; and some just try to create things and experiences that they could not have in the real world. Given the creativity that MOOs can unleash, researchers hope to adapt the basic technology for education and to help geographically remote workers create virtual open-plan offices in which they can collaborate as if they worked shoulder to shoulder.

MOTHERBOARD

A computer's central circuit board, into which plug the MICROPROCESSOR, MEMORY and other essential components of the machine. The motherboard provides the BUS which links together all of the computer's components, and is not to be confused with peripherals, enhancements or plug-in cards.

MOTIF

Extensions to the X WINDOWS system used on many a UNIX WORKSTATION. Motif was designed to make X better-looking and easier to use than the basic X system. Some say it succeeds.

MOUSE

The most popular form of pointing device for computers. Mice have a button or buttons on top and some kind of motion detector on the bottom. Move the mouse across the desktop and it moves an on-screen pointer, or CURSOR. Click a button and it selects the screen object underneath the cursor, to do whatever operation is appropriate in the given program at the given time.

The mouse was invented by Douglas Engelbart at Stanford Research Institute in the early 1970s, adopted by his neighbours down the road at Xerox's Palo Alto Research Center, and popularised by APPLE's MACINTOSH computer. For such humble devices, mice have sparked a surprising amount of discussion. Early mice had two buttons. Steve Jobs, who led the design of the Macintosh, insisted that its mouse have only one button, lest its users be overwhelmed by the difficulties of telling left from right. Most mice on a UNIX WORKSTATION, by contrast, have three buttons, because the nerds who run them insist on more choices.

MOVING PICTURES EXPERTS GROUP

See MPEG below.

MPEG

Sort for Moving Pictures Experts Group, standards which compress video and other moving pictures into a size that can be more easily stored on a CD-ROM or transmitted across a NETWORK. The grail of MPEG is so-called full-screen, full-motion video – which, as the name implies, would include every frame of motion at a size to cover a full screen.

MRP

Short for Materials Requirement Planning, a system commonly used to automate production scheduling, including ordering the appropriate raw materials.

MUD

Abbreviation for Multi-User Dungeon, a computerised version of fantasy role-playing games. Players take on a character, traditionally from the swords-and-sorcery selection of trolls, magicians, knights, and so on. Then they LOG ON to a central computer, where, by typing commands like north (to go north) or fight (to attack another character) they can wander blissfully through an imaginary world. MUDs were created at the University of Essex in the UK, but MUDs and MOOs, their more advanced relations, have since become one of the leading causes of computer addiction at campuses across the world.

For some people playing a character in a fantasy world can quickly become more interesting and compelling than classes, personal hygiene, or sleep. Campus folklore is now full of stories of promising students who sacrificed career and sanity for a chance of reaching wizard level (the highest) in the character of, say, Rotifer the Mag. Some university administrators have become so concerned about the amount of time students spend playing in a MUD that they have banned them from campus machines. Meanwhile, researchers elsewhere reckon that any technology which can so powerfully grip the human imagination must have some useful potential in it somewhere. So they are trying to use the principles of MUDs to design virtual worlds for collaboration among far-flung researchers (for more discussion of which see MOO).

MULTICAST

A form of broadcasting, adapted for efficiency on computer networks like the INTERNET. The problem with broadcasting over networks is that it wastes communications capacity. The obvious way of sending the same message to thousands of people is simply to send each a copy. But that means that many, perhaps thousands or millions, of copies of the same communication will clog the central backbone of the NETWORK, travelling one after the other. Multicasting tries to eliminate this inefficiency. The trick is to postpone the act of copying until the last possible moment, when communications routes to different destinations diverge. So, for example, if ten recipients are on the same

LOCAL AREA NETWORK, then multicasting will send only one copy of the message to the GATEWAY that links the local area network to the Internet. Copies will be created only on the local network, which greatly eases congestion. Experiments in multicasting have included attempts to deliver radio-style talk shows over the Internet.

MULTIMEDIA

Just what the word says: multimedia is the combination of different media – text, video, audio, graphics, and so on – with a bit of computing power to hold them all together. To deliver multimedia requires a high-BANDWIDTH communications channel, either NETWORK or CD-ROM. The hope, and hype, is that by combining different media, "authors" (or however multimediators are described) will be able to create things new and more wonderfully informative and educational than any yet dreamed of. The risk, of course, is that they will instead create a noisy, flashy mess.

The medium is the message. This is just to say that the personal and social consequences of any medium – that is, of any extension of ourselves – result from the new scale that is introduced into our affairs ...
Marshall McLuhan

MULTIPLEX

To combine several signals for transmission over the same communications channel. One of the most common forms of multiplexing is TIME DIVISION MULTIPLEXING, in which the channel is divided up by time slots. Each signal has its own series of very short time slots. From millisecond to millisecond, the multiplexor interleaves each signal's time slots with the others. Another commonly used form of multiplexing is FREQUENCY division multiplexing, in which each signal is assigned its own band of frequencies within the channel. The obvious point of multiplexing is to use channel capacity to maximum efficiency. Yet another form of multiplexing is code division multiple access or CDMA.

MULTI-PROCESSOR
Describes computers which share work among more than one MICROPROCESSOR. A modern FILE SERVER, for example, may use as many as six microprocessors. When there are many requests pending, it allocates tasks among microprocessors for fast service. When there are only a few, it gives each microprocessor a part of the task. This provides a cheap and flexible way of bringing maximum processing power to bear on a task.

MULTIPURPOSE INTERNET MAILING EXTENSIONS
See MIME.

MULTI-TASKING
Describes computers which execute several programs at once. Historically, the impetus for multi-tasking came from the observation that input and output typically took several orders of magnitude longer than any calculating the machine might do. Thus a typical program kept the CPU, the most expensive part of the computer, waiting for the vast majority of the time it occupied the machine. So some bright spark came up with the fairly obvious idea of sharing the CPU, letting programs with calculations ready to go use the CPU while others wait for input or output. When all goes well the result is a machine which appears to be at the personal command of several different people at once. When the machine gets overloaded – by too many people or too many calculation-intensive tasks – the result is annoying delays.

MUSICAL INSTRUMENT DIGITAL INTERFACE
See MIDI.

NACK

Negative Acknowledgement, which symbolises a code commonly used in communications protocols to denote that the message has been garbled or in some way messed up (contrast to ACK).

NAME SERVER

A computer on a NETWORK which translates mnemonic machine names and addresses, (used for example, to address E-MAIL) into the sequences of numbers machines use to talk to other machines.

NATIONAL TELEVISION STANDARDS COMMITTEE

See NTSC.

NC

See NETWORK COMPUTER.

NERD

Someone whose enthusiasm for playing with technology overshadows that for many other aspects of life, like socialising or washing. The archetypal nerd is male and dresses largely in polyester and plaid. His glasses are held together with a safety pin and spotted with dandruff. His pockets are full of felt-tip pens, calculators, paper clips and a small-office-worth of useful stuff. His wristwatch has more functions than most computers. Although nerds may not have had the most dates at school, many now have earnings that make their ex-classmates blush.

Anyone who spends their life on a computer is pretty unusual.
Bill Gates

NETIQUETTE

NETWORK manners. Like all human societies, computer networks have developed their own codes of conduct. Netiquette is a combination of the basic technical knowledge needed to avoid making a nuisance of yourself and common sense and respect for others.

NETSCAPE

A company making SOFTWARE used to view the global NETWORK of hypermedia that makes up the WORLD WIDE WEB. Netscape's WEB BROWSER became popular in part because the company gave the software away in the hope of building up a base of users to which it could sell other, more advanced services. But Netscape's lead in the browser market was soon being seriously challenged by Microsoft, with its Internet Explorer.

NETWORK

A collection of things or people linked together to share INFORMATION. Examples include the telephone network, the INTERNET, the Old Boy network, and so on.

NETWORK COMPUTER

A pared-down computer consisting of screen, keyboard and processor, but no DISK drive. Backers of the NC predict that it will become so cheap and easy to use that it will take over the world. Cynics see just a machine that does not do much, and does it slowly.

BANDWIDTH is the key to the success or failure of NCs. Because programs and DATA are stored centrally, it is crucial to be able to ship them back and forth quickly and seamlessly. In practice, this means that NCs may have a chance of success in the corporate market, because high-speed LANs already link the desktops of big companies. In this environment, storing data and programs centrally can create big savings on maintenance, BACK-UP and upgrades. In the home, though, obtaining sufficient bandwidth to power an NC is a real problem, as are the practicalities and economics of providing central storage for personal data.

NETWORK LAYER

That part of the SEVEN LAYER REFERENCE MODEL which concerns technologies for routing a PACKET from one machine to another across a NETWORK.

NEURAL NET

A way of computing based on the wiring of the brain rather than the symbolic reasoning of the mind. Neural nets are composed of many small processors connected together. These connections are the key to the workings of a neural net. The computing done by each processor node is quite simple. Each node either sends a signal or remains silent. That decision, in turn is based on the signals sent to the node. If the strength of the incoming signals is greater than some threshold value, the node sends its own signal to all of the nodes to which it is connected.

Neural nets are taught to recognise complex patterns by adjusting the strength of the signals between nodes, hence the effect that each node has on the others to which it is connected. Signals can either inhibit the firing of a node or promote it, and each signal can be given a weight, which determines how strongly it will inhibit or promote. Much of the recent enthusiasm for neural models of computation stems from the discovery of techniques for adjusting the weights on signals which can reliably enable the net to associate inputs with outputs, that is, to recognise patterns.

Neural nets are now being used to recognise handwriting, to search for patterns in stock-price movements and to recognise the road (and so help to build a car that can drive itself). The advantages of neural nets are twofold. They can recognise patterns far more complex than can be managed by conventional computers – faces, for example – and, because they use so many processors in parallel, they can do so quickly. Better still, the performance of neural nets degrades gracefully. They do not stop working all at once but instead, like people, simply make more and more errors as they encounter increasingly unfamiliar patterns.

Against these advantages, however, must be weighed the time and care that must be taken in training the nets: in successively showing them examples of right answers and wrong ones, and adjusting the connections between nodes to enable the net to distinguish one from the other. Another drawback of neural nets is their inability to explain how they have reached their conclusion. Because computation is spread across all of the processors that make up a net, there is no central consciousness which can explain to a sceptical observer how the net reached a given conclusion. This means that, in practice, using a neural net is quite literally an act of faith.

NEWS GROUP

An electronic forum for the discussion of a given topic. Tens of thousands of news groups now make up the USENET, a part of the INTERNET devoted to debate on topics ranging from sex to high-energy physics. News groups are open to all, and organised as an exchange of E-MAIL messages.

NEWS READER

A program used to read USENET news. News readers help to organise E-MAIL into a discussion of a specific subject. Mail is sorted by subject and time, so that someone entering the group discussion can follow the thread of electronic argument between many participants. Responses, in turn, are automatically sent to the proper address, with the proper subject.

NNTP

Short for Net News Transfer Protocol, the most commonly used PROTOCOL for transferring USENET news groups between one machine and another.

NOISE

Something which disrupts the flow of INFORMATION across a communications channel. The noisier a channel, the less information it can carry. The phrase "noise-to-signal ratio" refers to the relative quantities of each.

NOR

A logical operation performed in SOFTWARE or in circuitry. It returns true (or on) if and only if both inputs are false (or off); otherwise it returns false.

NOVELL

The name of a leading technology for creating a LOCAL AREA NETWORK with an IBM-COMPATIBLE computer and the company that makes it.

NSFNET

Refers to that portion of the INTERNET formerly funded by the USA's National Science Foundation (NSF). The NSF stopped financing the Internet in 1996, since when the network has supported itself commercially without the slightest stumble.

NTSC

Short for National Television Standards Committee, used to describe the technical standard for television transmissions in most of the Americas; although strictly, of course, the standard should be NTS, set by the NTSC. It makes up a picture of 525 lines of dots. (Contrast with PAL and SECAM.)

OBJECT DATABASE

An OBJECT-ORIENTED approach to storing DATA in a DATABASE. In addition to storing the data itself, object-oriented databases store INFORMATION about what can sensibly be done with the data. In effect, the object-oriented database tries to keep its data in context. It knows that a drawing from a COMPUTER AIDED DESIGN program is entirely different from last year's financial results, even if all the computer itself can see in both cases is a bunch of BITs.

OBJECT LINKING AND EMBEDDING

See OLE.

OBJECT ORIENTED

Describes an approach to programming first popularised in the 1980s with the language Smalltalk, which attempts to build programs out of SOFTWARE objects whose capabilities mirror those of the real world. For example, a "bank account" object, would store within itself its own balance, and it would know how to respond to messages making requests like "withdraw £50" or "deposit £1,000".

Three key ideas underlie this approach.

- Inheritance is a convenient way of capturing the similarities between things. All bank accounts share basic features in common. They have a balance, for example, and they must cope with money coming in and going out. Yet accounts also differ in other ways: how they calculate interest, or whether they offer an overdraft. Inheritance offers a way of sharing the common parts of an object, while still providing freedom for each object to add more specialised capabilities of its own. It saves time and money in large software projects. With inheritance, the common capabilities of a group of objects – like querying an account balance, for example – need be written only once; more specialised objects can then "inherit" that code. With inheritance, a designer can also enforce disciplines on the interface which objects present to the world; for example, by requiring that all "bank account" objects should at least be capable of taking a deposit or accepting a withdrawal, but without specifying exactly how.

- Polymorphism captures the idea that related objects might wish to do conceptually similar things in different ways. A cheque account with overdraft, for example, will deal with withdrawals differently from one without. In order to make polymorphism work in practice, it is crucial that no object should make assumptions about how another object does its work, apart from the necessary belief that, given a request and the necessary input, it will return a sensible answer. This in turn makes objects easier to modify, improve and change.

- Messages are the way in which things get done in an object-oriented world. Traditional programming languages talk about actions in terms of imperatives, that is, starting from the verb. So they would say something like "withdraw £50 from account X". But this approach sits uneasily with polymorphism because it leaves on the programmer's shoulders the responsibility for determining which of the many ways of making a withdrawal is appropriate for account X, and programmers often get it wrong. So object-oriented approaches put the noun in front of the verb to make the context clear. Instead of simply ordering an action, they send a message making a request: "Please, account X, do whatever it is you do when you make a withdrawal, in the amount of £50."

Although Smalltalk is still the purists' favourite object-oriented programming language, its popularity is being eclipsed by C++, a language that fits more easily into the environment in which object-oriented approaches thrive: the networked world of CLIENT-SERVER computing. The idea of sending messages to objects fits neatly into the world of distributed computing, where instead of with-drawing from a bank account, a program might send a message asking "please, PRINTER, print this with the highest quality you can manage". Given emerging standards like CORBA to help objects locate other objects with the capabilities they need, and negotiate to use them, object-oriented approaches could make even the biggest and most complex networks much more manageable.

OFFLINE

Lacking a NETWORK connection to another computer. In practice, it is a phrase most often used by a NERD as a synonym for "after the meeting", as in, "let's discuss that offline, after I've finished my presentation".

OLAP

Short for Online Analytic Processing, systems which make it possible for managers to view a cross-section of the firm's DATA, even as that data is being constantly updated. Contrast with OLTP systems, which are optimised for updating data, rather than analysing it.

OLE

Object Linking and Embedding, a STANDARD proposed by MICROSOFT which tries to apply OBJECT-ORIENTED technology to make it easier for computer programs to work together. If, for example, a chart from a SPREADSHEET is embedded in a document being word-processed, the standard helps the various SOFTWARE involved to know how and when to update the chart to reflect changes in the underlying spreadsheet. (See also OPENDOC.)

OLTP

Short for Online Transaction Processing, systems which make it possible for many people to record DATA on the same DATABASE at once. Typical OLTP systems are designed to enable users to work with one record at a time, for short periods of time. This is great for, say, recording sales in a database. But demands from managers wanting to analyse data, to seek correlations between many different records and transactions, have inspired the rise of ONLINE ANALYTIC PROCESSING, which is optimised for that sort of work.

ONLINE
The opposite of OFFLINE; that is, enjoying a NETWORK connection to another computer.

CompuServe and The Source became the first online information sources in 1979.

ONLINE ANALYTIC PROCESSING
See OLAP.

ONLINE TRANSACTION PROCESSING
See OLTP.

OPEN PROFILING STANDARD
A PROTOCOL designed to give people more control over the personal information gathered about them ONLINE. The Open Profiling Standard (OPS) defines ways for users to specify personal information – name, shoe size, favourite colour or whatever. It also defines ways for the user to specify what uses may be made of that information – whether it can be sold to third parties with the name attached, aggregated into anonymous group averages or whatever.

OPEN SYSTEM
One of the most abused phrases in information technology. Open system describes technology which is accessible for everybody to use, but as no one in their right mind would want to make their product inaccessible, everyone finds some way to shoe-horn their product into some definition of open system. So the word should be treated with some suspicion.

The most truly open system is probably UNIX (some people use open system as a synonym for Unix). Unix was developed by AT&T's Bell Labs while AT&T was still the USA's regulated telephone monopoly, and thus forbidden from commercially exploiting computer innovations. So the source code for Unix was freely distributed for all to explore and copy. For most open systems only a description of the INTERFACE – that is, the way in which the system interacts with other SOFTWARE and HARDWARE – is made publicly available. The completeness of that description determines how much hyperbole lies in its claims for openness.

OPENDOC
A technical STANDARD proposed by IBM, APPLE and others to make it easier for various pieces of SOFT-WARE to work together. If, say, a chart from a SPREADSHEET is embedded in a document from a WORD PROCESSOR, it enables the various software involved to know how and when to update the chart to reflect changes in the underlying spread-sheet. Despite its elegance, OpenDoc has been largely overtaken by MICROSOFT's OLE.

OPERATING SYSTEM
A key part of the infrastructure of computing, operating systems provide the basic capabilities from which applications can be built. In practice, this means hiding from applications SOFTWARE like word processors and spreadsheets many of the complexities of the machines they are working on. Among other things, operating systems typically manage the following.

- **MULTI-TASKING.** When programs share a CPU, the operating system is responsible for managing which program gets to run when.
- **Input and output.** Operating systems manage printers, tape drives and other input and output devices. Apart from administering the process of input and output – preventing programs from interfering with each other and monitoring whether printers and so on are working or not – they also provide a simplified INTERFACE which hides from the program the complexities of the HARDWARE of any input or

output device. This makes it easier to swap around peripherals as new models become available.

- **Files.** Managing the reading and writing of DATA to DISK is a form of input and output that takes up a huge proportion of the time and effort put into operating systems.
- MEMORY. The operating system loads programs into memory and ensures that they neither overlap nor interfere with each other's allocations of memory. Through techniques known as VIRTUAL MEMORY, some operating systems can run programs which are larger than the actual amount of memory in the machine. The trick is to swap parts of the program to and from disk as needed.
- **Networks.** Operating systems provide an interface to networks which, like other input and output interfaces, hides from applications programs much of the complexity of the underlying NETWORK.
- SECURITY. Operating systems enforce the security measures necessary to keep sensitive data secret, and to prevent even malicious users from messing up the work of their colleagues.
- SYSTEMS ADMINISTRATION. Perhaps the least interesting, but most important, features of any operating system are the tools provided for the housekeeping chores necessary to manage any computer system: to back up data, monitor and adjust performance and allocate scarce resources like disk space.

OPERATIONS RESEARCH

Techniques and disciplines aimed at making managerial decision-making more scientific. Operations research includes much of LINEAR PROGRAMMING, statistical reasoning and other mathematical techniques for finding optimal solutions to complex problems, where knowledge may be uncertain.

OPS

See OPEN PROFILING STANDARD.

Optical disk

A DISK in which DATA are read and written with a laser. The trick lies in finding materials that can be made reflective or not, repeatedly, quickly and easily. Early optical disks simply burnt away a reflective coating with a laser, making them into WORM disks, which could be written only once. With modern materials to create disks that can be written and rewritten repeatedly, the optical disk is gradually taking over from the TAPE DRIVE for storage of large quantities of data.

Or

An operation or circuit which returns true (or on) if one or more of its inputs is true (or on).

OS/2

IBM's next-generation OPERATING SYSTEM for the PERSONAL COMPUTER. OS/2 is personal computing's great might-have-been. It is a MULTI-TASKING operating system with a graphical INTERFACE which is by most accounts technically excellent. Yet it has received only lukewarm acceptance in the marketplace. Whatever its virtues, OS/2 has been consistently overshadowed by MICROSOFT's WINDOWS family of operating systems.

Microsoft originally worked with IBM to develop OS/2, but it broke up the partnership in 1990 because it thought its customers preferred the simplicity of Windows to the new capabilities of OS/2. It was right. By the time the two had split Microsoft had grabbed the momentum in the marketplace with strong sales of Windows which, unlike OS/2, was already shipping. Microsoft kept that momentum to establish Windows NT, a MULTI-TASKING version of Windows, as the the rival to UNIX for corporate file servers and other demanding applications – and, eventually, as the probable successor to Windows for the domination of the desktop.

PABX

Short for Private Automatic Branch Exchange, a privately owned and operated telephone switch which serves as the switchboard for a typical office. PABXs typically handle tens or hundreds of lines, and, unlike old-fashioned switchboards, they do so without requiring banks of operators manually to plug one line into another.

PACKET

A way of organising DATA for communication. Instead of a steady stream of BITs and BYTEs, most computer communications split data into discrete packets. As well as data, each packet typically contains the address to which the packet is being sent, a number which denotes that packet's place in the sequence, and information which helps to detect and correct errors. Some packets also contain information about what type of data is being sent. Others serve administrative functions in setting up routes and managing the flow of data.

The advantage of packets is their flexibility and efficiency. Packets from different communications can easily be intermixed to maximise use of a line. Packets from the same communication can travel by different routes to speed passage over a crowded network. Given the speed of today's computers, packets can easily carry time-sensitive data, like interactive video, or voice conversations. But the drawback to packet data is, nonetheless, the extra overhead of splitting data into packets at one end and recombining them at the other.

PACKET-SWITCHED

Describes a NETWORK that sends DATA one PACKET at a time, and so does not keep open a connection between two machines when no data is flowing between them. For many applications, particularly with computer data, the extra overheads of addressing each packet separately are well worth the savings in efficiency gained from not holding open temporarily unused connections. (Contrast to CIRCUIT-SWITCHED.)

PAGING

A way of managing VIRTUAL MEMORY, in which standard sized chunks of program and/or DATA are swapped into MEMORY when needed and temporarily stashed back on DISK when not. Because paging is a relatively slow operation and does not contribute directly to the progress of computation, how a computer manages paging is a key issue in its overall performance. Paging is also a system for mobile communications whereby a simple message is sent to a pocket terminal.

PAL

Short for Phase Alteration by Line, a colour television STANDARD developed in the UK and used there and in Germany. It makes up a picture with 625 lines of dots. (Contrast to NTSC and SECAM.)

PARALLEL COMMUNICATIONS

Describes a form of communications in which several BITs are sent simultaneously, in contrast to SERIAL communications in which they are sent one after the other. The extra speed of parallel communications has made it popular for sending DATA to printers, but the fine timing required to make sure that all the bits arrive at the same time limits its use to fairly short distances. Hence also parallel PORT, the connection where the wires for parallel communications are plugged in.

PARALLEL PROCESSING

Attacking the same problem with several processors at once. Like the proverb, the assumption behind parallel processing is that "many hands make light work".

A rough and ready classification of parallel processing would divide into three categories.

- **Multiprocessing.** Many file servers, for example, share their work among half a dozen or so processors. When one is overloaded, another lends a helping hand.
- **Parallel supercomputers.** Machines from N-Cube, INTEL and a variety of other com-

panies aim for high-speed computation by putting tens or hundreds of processors to work on the same problem. Such machines are used to forecast the weather, analyse stress on aircraft wings and search vast databases quickly. The processors can work either in strict synchronisation (see SIMD) or with a looser co-ordination in which the problem is split into several chunks, and each processor tackles its chunks at its own speed (see MIMD).

- **Neural nets.** A NEURAL NET contains hundreds or even thousands of simple processors. While the capabilities of each individual processor are limited, the connections between them enable neural nets to recognise complex patterns.

Although parallel processing can indeed improve results on many problems, researchers face two challenges in taking advantage of its full potential. The first is simply the intellectual sweat of recasting the solutions to problems in a form that allows different parts of the work to be done simultaneously. Second, and hardest, those solutions must ensure that the time spent co-ordinating results among different processors does not overwhelm the extra speed gained from having more "brains" at work. Some people feel that such co-ordination problems will place the ultimate limits on the extra speed to be gained from parallelisation. Others are hard at work trying to crack those limits.

In 1958 the Harvard Business Review *predicted that the economy of the 1980s would be dominated by a handful of giant corporations, each organised around a single huge computer.*

PARITY

Describes a scheme for detecting and correcting errors in which each piece of DATA is required to have an even or odd number of BITs. If the number naturally comes out the wrong way, an extra BIT, called the parity bit, is turned on to make it right. This scheme should detect all one-bit errors, or indeed all errors involving an odd number of bits. But it is not much good for two-bit errors. Nevertheless, its speed and ease of use has made it popular for monitoring computer MEMORY.

PASCAL
A programming language created by a Swiss computer scientist, Niklaus Wirth. For most of the 1980s it was the first language taught to young computer scientists, and it has been highly influential in shaping ideas about STRUCTURED PROGRAMMING and the proper style of a program. The simplicity that makes it excellent for teaching, however, has limited its use in real, workaday programming.

PASSWORD
A sequence of characters which serves as a kind of text key in gaining access to computers. To maintain SECURITY, passwords should be known only to their owners and be hard to guess.

PATCH
A correction or improvement to a program that is distributed as a snippet of code, together with instructions on how and where the new code is to be stitched into the old program.

PC
See PERSONAL COMPUTER.

PC-COMPATIBLE
See IBM-COMPATIBLE.

PCI
Short for Peripheral Components Interface, a fast computer BUS, quick enough for both video and graphics, which is now becoming standard on IBM-COMPATIBLE computers.

PCMCIA

Abbreviation for Personal Computer Memory Card International Association, a series of technical standards for the creation of small (as small as credit-card sized) circuit boards that can be plugged into personal computers to add a MODEM, networking capabilities or other enhancements.

PDA

Short for Personal Digital Assistant, a form of computer which is meant to fit into a jacket pocket (well, given a very large jacket) and travel everywhere with its owner. Progenitor of the breed was APPLE's Newton, a machine designed to do several useful things at once, including the following.

- **Communications.** Using either a wireless MODEM or a plug into the telephone network, PDAs can send and receive faxes, E-MAIL and DATA.
- **Diary.** PDAs typically come equipped with SOFTWARE to manage appointments and to keep track of addresses and other personal information.
- **Notes.** PDAs are also typically designed to take and store notes, and to write simple memos and letters.

So far so useful. But the snag with PDAs is getting information into the machines in the first place. Designers of the original PDAs assumed that technology for handwriting recognition – that is, for a computer automatically and accurately to convert human scrawl into ASCII characters – would make PDAs the first of a new breed of pen-based computers. But the inaccuracy of handwriting technology made early PDAs a joke instead of a success. Unfortunately, any keyboard small enough to fit into a jacket pocket is also too small to use comfortably.

PEERING

The arrangements under which one company will transmit DATA packets originating on another com-

pany's networks. Because the INTERNET is a NET-
WORK of networks, all owned by different companies, peering is crucial to its operation.

The pioneers of the Internet all carried each
other's packets without any attempt at charging or
ensuring equal costs or service. If they had not
nothing would have got anywhere. As the Internet
has grown and matured, though, peering arrangements have grown more complicated and more
vexed. The basic principles are simple: charge if
you can, but do not offend anyone big enough to
retaliate in a way that will inconvenience your
customers. Needless to say, the real skill of these
principles is in the implementation.

PEN-BASED COMPUTING
Computers that take their input from a pen-like
stylus rather than a keyboard. Characters and text-
based DATA would be input through HANDWRITING
RECOGNITION, whereby the computer translated
human scrawl into ASCII characters. Graphics and
free-hand drawings could be stored using DIGITAL
ink; that is, by simply recording the path of the
stylus over the screen as a sequence of BITS and
BYTES. Commands to the computer would often
come in the form of gestures, like ticks (to choose
from a MENU) or the proof-reader's deletion mark.

Unfortunately the general inadequacy of early
handwriting recognition programs meant that
pen-based computers failed to live up to their
early hype. They have nonetheless proved extremely useful in helping mobile workers, like
warehouse staff and insurance claims adjusters, to
automate many of the forms they fill in.

PENTIUM
The successor to INTEL's 80486 microprocessors,
Pentium chips owe their name to the vagaries of
trademark law. Numbers, reckon US courts, are
not trademarks. So Intel's competitors could call
their cloned versions of its 80486 chip by the same
name. Not so the Pentium, which is Intel's own.

PERIPHERAL

A device which attaches to a computer; for example, a PRINTER, TAPE DRIVE, PLOTTER, external DISK drive, or the like.

In 1982 Time *named the personal computer its man of the year.*

PERSONAL COMPUTER

A computer designed to serve one person only, in contrast to the MAINFRAME or MINICOMPUTER which used MULTI-TASKING operating systems and networks of terminals to serve many people at once. The original personal computers (PCs) were created by hobbyists who were at least as interested in how the machines worked as in what they could do, like the members of Silicon Valley's Homebrew Computer Club, the hang-out of Steve Wozniak and Steve Jobs, founders of APPLE. Most big computer companies turned up their noses at the machines, seeing no advantage over minicomputers or mainframes. They were wrong.

As advances in SEMICONDUCTOR technology have made possible more and more complex microprocessors and cheaper and cheaper MEMORY, both economics and convenience are pushing computing power on to individual's desktops, into their pockets and wherever else it can fit. Many executives now carry in their briefcases more computing power than a 1970s mainframe. They need not follow corporate procedures, or ask permission, to get the resources needed for complex computations, or to create high-quality presentations and letters. They own them. At the same time, networks often enable disparate executives to share information, when they wish to, almost as quickly and conveniently as can be achieved by established procedures. So the personal computer has helped to break down the centrally administered and controlled world of the mainframe in favour of a management style that promotes individual initiative and flexible cooperation.

PGP

Short for Pretty Good Privacy. PGP began as a freely distributed implementation of the RSA ALGORITHM for public-key encryption, created by Phil Zimmerman. PGP is controversial for several reasons. It has been distributed internationally in defiance of a US export ban on SOFTWARE containing technology for PUBLIC-KEY CRYPTOGRAPHY. It was also distributed without the permission of the holders of the patent on the RSA algorithm. Yet it works and, for those concerned with privacy, PGP is the most secure way of keeping computer DATA from prying eyes. In late 1996 Zimmerman founded a company, also called PGP, to commercialise and further improve the technology he created.

PHASE

ANALOGUE communications signals are typically built upon CARRIER waves which, as the name suggests, vary rhythmically up and down, positive and negative. Phase refers to where in the cycle, up or down, the wave is. One way of coding INFORMATION into a carrier wave is to alter the phase; that is, to push it up when it would naturally be down.

PHREAKER

A HACKER who concentrates on the telephone system, breaking into corporate voice mail, for example, or using tone-generators to get free international calls. It derives from phone-freak.

PHYSICAL LAYER

That part of the SEVEN LAYER REFERENCE MODEL which concerns the technology used to transmit signals across a communications channel, such as radio waves, electric pulses, light, and so on.

PICS

Short for Platform for Internet Content Selection. One of the coolest, smartest ideas yet to arrive on the INTERNET, PICS was created to give parents, schools and others some control over the sorts of stuff that children can see on the Internet. But it can be used for any sort of ratings system, from consumer reports to film reviews. What's wonderful about PICS is that it offers this control without imposing a single set of standards for appropriate viewing, like television or film ratings systems.

PICS takes advantage of the fact that, on the Internet, everything is connected to everything else. So it is possible for anybody to create ratings of anything, and for anybody else to use those ratings to guide their browsing. Instead of simply pulling down a Web page to the screen, most Web browsers can now be configured to check the rating of the page in question first, from whichever Web site maintains the ratings that the user chooses to trust. If the rating is one the user wishes to exclude, which can be any level measurable by the rating system, then the WEB BROWSER does not display the page.

One of most popular ratings systems, called RSACi, bases its ratings on three criteria: sex, violence and language. Ratings in each category are determined by answering an interactive questionnaire at the RSAC Web site (*www.rsac.org*). But unlike film ratings systems, which collapse judgment into a single recommendation of the appropriate age for viewers, RSACi reports each rating separately, allowing parents who might be worried about violence but not sex (or vice versa) more control over what their children watch.

In theory, PICS ratings systems can be concocted with whatever criteria anybody might want, from potential offensiveness to, say, the privacy policies followed on a Web site or the reliability of information posted there. One measure of PICS' success will be its ability to make unneccessary government threats to censor the Internet. The other will be number of ratings systems it inspires; in other words, the extent to which it encourages anybody with burning convictions to be not just a consumer of information but also a producer of informed judgments.

PICT

A technical STANDARD for storing graphics files, commonly used on MACINTOSH personal computers.

PIXEL

Acronym for picture element, or the dots which make up an image on the typical computer screen. Black and white images need only one BIT per pixel, but colour images require that each pixel be represented by a BINARY number. With a BYTE, or eight bits, for each pixel, a screen can contain up to 256 different colours. With 24 bits for each pixel, it can contain 16,777,216 different colours – the biggest number 24 bits can express.

PLASMA DISPLAY

A form of computer screen which lights pixels on the screen by passing an electric current through a tiny bubble of gas, causing it to emit light. Plasma screens are compact and bright. But they are also power-hungry and often come in ugly colours.

PLOTTER

A device used for output of line drawings – usually engineering and architectural plans – which typically works by drawing a kind of pen across the surface of a piece of paper.

PLUG COMPATIBLE

A piece of equipment that conforms to the same technical standards as that of another manufacturer. So getting the one to work with the other is as easy as plugging them in. Originally the term referred to a variety of equipment made to work with IBM mainframes, and thus to compete against IBM's versions of the same products.

PLUG-IN

A small piece of SOFTWARE that attaches to a larger program to extend its capabilities. By far the most popular use of plug-ins is on Web browsers, where popular plug-ins play movies, provide CD-quality sound, and create animation or even three-dimensional virtual worlds.

POINTCAST

The company which commercialised PUSH MEDIA.

As with many path-breakers, Pointcast's name is often used synonymously with its creation: a ticker-tape-like stream of constantly updated INFORMATION, scrolling along the bottom of a computer screen.

POINTER
In programming, pointers "point" to the location in MEMORY where a piece of DATA is stored.

POLLING
A way of monitoring inputs in which the CPU checks each periodically to see if anything new has arrived. (Contrast to INTERRUPT-driven, in which the inputs demand attention from the CPU.)

POP
Post Office Protocol, a STANDARD for managing the local delivery of E-MAIL from a central server to its many clients. It is used by Eudora, a popular e-mail program.

PORT
Where input or output happens. For example, a NETWORK port handles DATA coming in from, or going out to, a network; a PRINTER port handles traffic for a printer.

POSTSCRIPT
A computer language used to describe to a PRINTER what a page should look like. Postscript was created by John Warnock, who founded Adobe Systems to manufacture and market it. Dr Warnock had worked on computer graphics since his doctoral thesis at the University of Utah, which described quick ways of sketching two-dimensional views of three-dimensional objects. He designed Postscript to be quick and convenient in specifying shapes, fonts, spacing and layout.

Originally he had thought that Postscript would require too much expensive computer MEMORY to work in any but professional typesetting systems. But in 1983 Steve Jobs of APPLE convinced him that memory prices would fall far enough to enable the language to be incorporated into a low-cost LASER PRINTER. This is exactly what they did, and Dr Warnock spent many sleepless nights worrying that his fledgling firm would run out of money before the HARDWARE needed to support his product could be built. In the end Dr Warnock was rewarded for his bravery with one of the most consistently profitable products in the history of computing.

POTS

Short for Plain Old Telephone Service, where you pick up the phone, dial and speak – no more, no less.

PowerPC

A design for RISC chips backed by IBM and APPLE for high-powered PCs. Now used in all of Apple's MACINTOSH personal computers, PowerPC chips offer more raw speed than the INTEL PENTIUM processors used in PC-compatible machines.

PPP

Point to Point Protocol, technical standards that enable the use of the INTERNET's communication protocols, TCP/IP, over a dial-up telephone line. (An alternative to SLIP.)

Activism is the killer app for the Net.
Steven Cherry

PRESENTATION LAYER

That part of the SEVEN LAYER REFERENCE MODEL which concerns technologies for encryption, COMPRESSION and encoding DATA being sent across a NETWORK.

PRINTED CIRCUIT BOARD

A way of linking together electronic components without wires. Printed circuit boards consist of strips of conducting metal laid on a (non-conducting) base of epoxy by a process akin to printing. The strips substitute for wires. They typically begin and end in small holes, into which plug stiff wires (called connectors) which protrude from SEMICONDUCTOR chips. Printed circuit boards make it possible to reproduce complex wiring in high volumes at low cost.

PRINTER

A device that enables a computer to output its DATA on to paper. Common types include INK-JET PRINTER, MATRIX PRINTER and LASER PRINTER.

PRIVATE KEY

Like all cryptographic keys, these determine how a message will be encoded. Unlike other cryptographic keys, those used in PUBLIC KEY CRYPTOGRAPHY come as a pair, each of which can decrypt messages encrypted with the other key. The private key, predictably, is the one that is kept secret. Public keys, by contrast, are known to all, so that anybody can encrypt a message that can be decrypted with the corresponding private key.

Because encrypting messages with a private key is the way in which a DIGITAL SIGNATURE is made, and identity is established in CYBERSPACE, security of private keys is extremely important. One of the many reasons KEY ESCROW schemes are such a bad idea is that they would compromise an individual's control over the security of his private key, and thus his digital identity.

PROCESS

In technology-speak, a process is a running program. In the world of business, a process is some group of activities – typically involving both men and machines – which achieves some goal. Thus there might be a product-delivery process, which gets products to the customer, and a new manager might re-engineer that process to achieve the same goals by different (and it is hoped better) means.

PROLOG

See LOGIC PROGRAMMING.

PROM

Short for Programmable, Read-Only Memory, a

chip that can store programs or DATA indefinitely. Writing data to a PROM requires special equipment, but once there the data remain even with the power switched off. PROMs are widely used to store and distribute the programs which control electronic devices like modems, calculators and the like. In computers, PROMs typically store the BOOT-STRAP code which enables the machine to find and run its OPERATING SYSTEM (which, in turn, enables it to find and run other programs). (See also EPROM.)

PROTOCOL

A kind of canned dialogue that enables two computers to negotiate, even when they have no idea of the meaning of the symbols that they are sending back and forth. For example, a protocol might specify the sequence of commands which one computer uses to send E-MAIL to another: what to say when a message is coming, how to reply after it has been received, and so on. While humans can make up dialogues as they go along, computers can only stick to the scripts laid down for them in the protocol.

PSTN

Short for Public Switched Telephone Network, a commercial telephone NETWORK.

PTT

Abbreviation for Post, Telephone and Telegraph, usually used to refer to state-owned monopolies which operate most countries' telecommunications, as distinct from the diverse collection of telecoms-service providers which compete for customers in, for example, the USA and the UK.

PUBLIC KEY

See PRIVATE KEY.

PUBLIC-KEY CRYPTOGRAPHY

The technology which makes electronic commerce possible. Public-key encryption overcomes the major weaknesses of earlier codes and ciphers: the difficulty of exchanging a key between coder and decoder. Each code has a key which specifies how the message was encoded, and, in turn, how it can be decoded. Should that key fall into prying hands, the coded message can easily be read, hence the plot of many spy novels.

Public-key encryption solves the problem of communicating the key by splitting it into two parts. One part is public, and can be listed in something like a telephone directory. The second is private, and should be told to nobody. To send a secret message, encrypt the text with the public key of the intended recipient. Then only someone with that person's PRIVATE KEY will be able to decode it. Equally a message can be given a DIGITAL SIGNATURE, to ensure that it does indeed come from the person whose name is at the top, by encrypting it with that person's PRIVATE KEY, and then decrypting it with the corresponding public key.

The mathematics underlying public-key cryptography is complex, and involves large prime numbers. But so far these are some of the few encryption techniques that cannot reliably be broken by code-breakers using supercomputers. The effectiveness of the code is proportional to the size of the numbers used as the keys. Keys with numbers tens of bits long create codes that can be broken quite easily. Anything over 1,000 bits is reckoned to be unbreakable.

To maintain its ability to eavesdrop on the communications of its enemies, the US government has led a global campaign to limit the use of encryption. It bans the export of encryption technology using keys with large numbers of bits (that is, effective keys). It backs KEY ESCROW schemes which would require users of encryption to deposit their private keys with a TRUSTED THIRD PARTY, which in turn is required to hand them over to security agencies. Asserting a right to wiretap seems morally wrong, rather like requiring locksmiths to keep copies of the keys and combinations for every safe they install. It also undermines the growth of electronic commerce, by compromising the security encryption can bring to CYBERSPACE. It is also pointless. Solid public-key encryption is already available from any number of sources, ranging from the hackers who created PGP to the Finnish computer scientists who founded Data Fellows and the Russian defence scientists who have founded companies like Elvis+, whose encryption technology is used by SUN MICROSYSTEMS and others for customers outside the USA who would otherwise fall foul of US export regulations covering encryption.

PUNCHED CARD

A computing relic. Instead of disks, early computer programs and DATA were stored by punching holes out of stiff paper cards. Probably the most common card format stored about 80 characters. Cards were read horizontally, like text. The computer determined which number or character was at each position in the text by the vertical location of the hole punched in the cards. While modern programmers complain about a DISK CRASH, old timers know that there are few greater frustrations than dropping a carefully typed deck of cards on to the floor.

> *In 1947 Tom Watson Sr quashed IBM's plans for its first computer which would store data on magnetic tape because he preferred storing data on punched cards, where it could be seen.*

PUSH MEDIA

Content that comes to you. One of the joys of the INTERNET and the WORLD WIDE WEB is that it enables anybody to go out and find just the material they want, from the combined resources of the whole world. The drawback is that the joy of the search may quickly become drudgery when you know exactly what you want, but the technology of the Internet still makes you go out and fetch it every time you want it. Hence push media, which offer a variety of ways of subscribing to content for regular delivery to your DISK.

Strictly, E-MAIL was the first push medium, but

the technology has since been created to push out Web pages, with all their embedded graphics and links. POINTCAST started the rush into new forms of push media with a streaming ticker of news headlines which rolled across the bottom of a computer screen. The Pointcast NETWORK rapidly grew to encompass content from a variety of sources, ranging from the *Wall Street Journal* to company news from IBM. But Pointcast has been challenged by Marimba, founded by some members of the team that created JAVA at SUN MICROSYSTEMS. Marimba's CASTANET SOFTWARE enables anybody to create their own channel of push media. So it is used by, for example, Aetna insurance company to keep sales agents up-to-date with company policy as well as by publishers trying to reach a mass market.

Push media eases one of the greatest headaches faced by would-be Web advertisers: knowing who is viewing the ads they pay to place on the screen. Having surfed through once, there is no guarantee that any visitor to a standard Web site will ever return. Subscribers to push media, by contrast, have made a commitment to get material downloaded to their disk regularly, advertisements and all. Advertisers like that.

QUERY
Noun or verb describing a request for information to a DATABASE.

QUICKSORT
A commonly used routine to sort DATA into some order: alphabetical, ascending by number, or whatever.

QUICKTIME
A technology developed by APPLE Computer to display video, play sound and generally help to create MULTIMEDIA computers.

QWERTY
Describes the most popular form of keyboard, which is distinguished by the sequence of keys on the first alphabetic row: q, w, e, r, t and y. Time and motion studies have shown that the layout of the QWERTY keyboard is less than optimal. Characters that frequently occur together in text are placed far apart on the keyboard, forcing unnecessary movement. Although more efficient keyboards have been designed, like the Dvorak keyboard, none have yet seriously challenged the dominance of the familiar QWERTY layout.

Radix

The basis of a number system; that is, the number which the system counts in. In a BINARY system the radix is 2, in DECIMAL 10 and in HEXADECIMAL 16.

RAID

Redundant Array of Inexpensive Disks, a way of creating the capacity to store huge quantities of DATA by using a bunch of fairly small disks in unison. The clever trick is stringing the data across the disks so that if one fails a BACK-UP can automatically take its place.

RAM

Short for Random Access Memory, the MEMORY chips used in most computers. RAM stores DATA on an array of transistors. Each element of the array is accessed by location. If the transistor at a given location holds a charge it is interpreted as a BINARY 1, if not then 0.

RAM is quick. Its data can be accessed in billionths of a second, and data can be accessed equally quickly anywhere in the array. RAM is rapidly growing more capacious. By the late 1990s chips storing over 64m BITS of information were commonplace, and SEMICONDUCTOR laboratories were producing chips storing 256m bits. (Simple geometry insists that memory-chip capacity will always grow by multiples of four; if you double the number of circuits that can fit on each side of a rectangle …)

There are two common sorts of RAM. DRAM is cheap and easy to use, but it requires a constant electric current or it forgets. SRAM is quicker and more permanent, but also more expensive.

Raster

Describes the most commonly used scheme for the display of text and images on computer screens and printers. Raster screens and printers create lines and images by way of a fixed array of dots, each of which can be coloured, or not, as needed. Early computer screens, and today's plotters, by contrast, displayed images by drawing lines with a pen or electron beam, much as a person would.

The advantage of moving from line to raster, as the arrays of dots are called, is speed of display. It is quick and easy for a computer to scan through a sequence of bytes in MEMORY and colour corresponding dots on screen according to the value found in each BYTE; much quicker and easier than drawing a sequence of lines of varying colour, thickness and orientation.

A disadvantage, however, is that in the transfer to raster form, some lines acquire a stepped, jagged appearance, particularly in low-resolution devices (which use comparatively few dots per inch). A second disadvantage is that raster images typically require much more memory to store. Only a few bytes are required to remember the thickness and end points of a line, but to store all the points along and around the line requires much more. But with memory prices continually falling, the speed and convenience of raster technology overshadows its hunger for memory.

REAL NUMBER

Includes both INTEGERS and numbers with a finite number of digits to the right of a decimal point.

REAL TIME

Describes computer systems, usually used to control machinery, which have stringent limits on the time that they can devote to any computation. Most computer systems simply compute until they have finished with a given calculation. The systems helping to navigate a jet fighter, by contrast, cannot ponder their position for too long or the plane will hit something before they are done.

Designers of real-time systems devote much time and energy to calculating in advance just how long any given computation might take, to ensure that it does not disrupt the process of control. This, in turn, breeds a keen appreciation of just how best to balance accuracy and speed in any given situation. Calculating the height of a mountain to greater accuracy offers little reward after the plane has crashed into it. Yet while cruising at altitude an engine control system can profitably devote itself to micro-management of fuel consumption.

RECORD
The basic unit of information stored in a DATABASE. Each record stores all of the information relevant to a particular entry. Databases are composed of records, and records, in turn, are composed of fields, each of which stores part of a record. For example, a customer record might have fields to store name, address, and so on.

RE-ENGINEERING
Rapid, dramatic change to the way a business does its work, typically enabled by the capabilities of new technology. The re-engineering movement's manifesto was an article written in the *Harvard Business Review* by Michael Hammer entitled "Don't Automate, Obliterate". The point of the article was that new technology often enabled work to be done so dramatically differently that many companies would be better off ignoring efforts to improve what they do now, and instead they should simply start over again from scratch.

During the 1990s more and more companies did just that. Three themes ran through their work.

- **A shift from sequential work to simultaneous work.** With information on paper, only one person can easily access it at a time; on a DATABASE, by contrast, many can do so at once. So many companies are collapsing time-consuming, step-by-step procedures into speedy parallel ones.
- **Worker empowerment.** The whole point of employing a decision-maker lies in not telling him or her what decisions to make. So managing shifts from telling people what to do to coaching them into higher performance.
- **A process view of organisation.** Traditionally, managers have thought about

how work gets done in their organisations, laying down detailed procedures for each task. Increasingly, re-engineered organisations focus on what is to be done, leaving empowered workers to decide for themselves how these goals can best be met.

REGISTER

Within a MICROPROCESSOR, registers hold the DATA and instructions presently being worked with. The size of the register helps to determine the power and capacity of the microprocessor, for the obvious reason that it determines how much data can be worked on at once. Thus so-called 16-BIT computers have registers that can hold 16 bits at a time; 32-bit computers have registers that can hold 32 bits. By the late 1990s most personal computers had evolved from the 16-bit registers of the original IBM PC to 32-bit microprocessors, and 64-bit machines were becoming common.

RELATIONAL DATABASE

Today's most commonly used technology for storing INFORMATION and DATA, the relational database was created by E.F. Codd at IBM in the 1970s. He based the technology on a mathematical theory of relations, which ensured that each piece of data had one, and only one, place in the DATABASE.

Relational databases store information in tables. One or more columns are the index of the table, that is, the key by which information is looked up when needed. Every other piece of data (that is, the other entries on each row) is associated with an index. There are two basic operations on these tables. Filtering the data strips out that which meets (or does not meet) some criteria; for example, all salespeople living in London. A JOIN combines data from different tables. For example, a join between quarterly sales figures (indexed by salesperson's name) and a table of salespeople's addresses (also indexed by name) might be helpful if management wanted to send each salesperson a summary of recent performance.

REMOTE PROCEDURE CALL

A PROTOCOL which enables a computer to execute a program on a remote computer, linked across a NETWORK, and then to retrieve the result of that computation.

RENDERING

Describes the process of drawing a surface on a computer graphic. A computer-generated model is typically built in two steps. A WIRE-FRAME MODEL defines the basic skeleton of the object. Then rendering draws a realistic surface skin over the skeleton to make the object appear to be solid, appropriately textured and appropriately shaded.

RESERVATION PROTOCOL

See RSVP.

RESERVED WORD

One of the words with special meaning in a given programming language. Because reserved words tell the computer to do something, they cannot sensibly be used as names for variables or other DATA. Using a reserved word in programming is a bit like calling a dog Sit, which causes obvious problems in training Sit to sit.

RESET

To return a computer to the state in which it normally finds itself when the power is first switched on. This is a useful last resort when a BUG has caused a program to enter an infinite LOOP, or if for some other reason it will not respond to input.

RFC

Short for Request for Comments, one of the documents used by the IETF to reach consensus on technical standards and other INTERNET policy matters. Typically, RFCs are numbered, so RFC1661, for example, defines the PPP PROTOCOL, while RFC1855 discusses guidelines for NETIQUETTE.

RGB MONITOR

Red Green Blue monitor, a colour MONITOR that

accepts red, green and blue signals separately, and thereby produces sharper images than a COMPOSITE MONITOR, which mixes them together.

RICH TEXT FORMAT

A FILE format created by MICROSOFT to exchange documents between its WORD PROCESSOR, Word, and others, while maintaining fonts, margins and other formatting.

RISC

Short for Reduced Instruction Set Computing, a new philosophy of MICROPROCESSOR design which promises to make much faster and more powerful computers. RISC chips are a tribute to the virtues of simplicity in information technology.

In the 1970s microprocessor designers reasoned that, as most operations are more quickly performed in HARDWARE than in SOFTWARE, the more different functions they could put on to a chip, the faster programs would run. So they devoted their energies to packing more and more functions on to chips.

Then researchers at IBM decided to examine how a representative sample of programs used the functions being packed on to the chips, to see which they should try to optimise. They discovered that programs used intensively only a small number of simple functions, and did not use many of the more complex instructions at all. Worse, the extra circuitry and rigmarole needed to pack the complex instructions on to the chips slowed the chips down.

So researchers from IBM and elsewhere began designing microprocessors which offered only a few functions, basically simple arithmetic, comparisons for larger or smaller and manipulating BITs to turn them on or off. Programs grew larger because the new RISC chips required more of their simple instructions to do useful work. But because they devoted all their circuitry to running simple instructions very, very fast, RISC chips were quicker than the CISC chips that preceded them.

In the late 1990s four different RISC designs led

the battle for market share: SUN MICROSYSTEMS' SPARC, IBM's POWERPC (which was also used by APPLE for a new generation of MACINTOSH computers), Hewlett Packard's Precision architecture and the MIPS chip, backed mostly by workstation-makers like Silicon Graphics. INTEL, for its part, joined with Hewlett Packard to create possible RISC successors to its best-selling range of microprocessors.

ROM

Short for Read-Only Memory; as the name says, MEMORY that can be read but only written using special machinery (usually at the factory). It comes in many formats. Two of the most common are CD-ROM, on compact disks, and PROM, on SEMI-CONDUCTOR chips. It is considerably more useful than write-only memory.

ROUNDING ERRORS

The arithmetical errors caused by trying to cram real-life numbers, which can have unlimited digits, into the fixed confines of the arbitrary space that most SOFTWARE allocates in computer MEMORY to hold them.

ROUTER

A device which connects two distinct local area networks using the same technical protocols. (Contrast with BRIDGE, which connects local area networks using different protocols.)

RS-232

RS stands for Requirements Specification in the names of this series of standards for DATA communication created by the USA's Institute of Electrical Engineers. Perhaps the best known of the series is RS-232, which dictates how most personal computers work with modems. The STANDARD lays down such mundane but crucial things as how the MODEM tells the computer it is ready to receive data, how it signals that a connection has been made (or lost), and so on.

RS-422

An improved specification that is gradually replacing RS-232.

RSA ALGORITHM

The most widely used technique for PUBLIC-KEY CRYPTOGRAPHY, named after the initials of its creators, three academics at the Massachusetts Institute of Technology: Rivest, Shamir and Adelman.

RSACI

One of the most popular systems of ratings created for the PICS standard, RSACi was designed to help schools and parents keep children away from potentially offensive material on the INTERNET. RSAC stands for the Recreational Software Advisory Council, a group created to rate computer games for gore, sex, dirty language and all the other things that parents disapprove of; the "i" indicates that this is their effort for the Internet. RSACi rates each Web site on three different criteria: sex, violence and language. Because PICS allows ratings on each criteria to be given separately, parents worried about violence but not sex, or vice versa, have a fair amount of control over the material that will be automatically be shielded from their children's inquiring gaze.

RSVP

One of technology's more tortured acronyms, RSVP stands for ReSerVation Protocol. It is an effort to improve quality of service over the INTERNET by allowing sender or receiver to ask for a certain amount of BANDWIDTH to be set aside for their exclusive use.

For most of the packets transmitted over the Internet, there is no guarantee of quality of service whatsoever. Net protocols simply try to find the best possible route for each PACKET, packet by packet, until the transmission is complete. If all routes are clogged, the packet is simply dropped. This works surprisingly well for e-mail, where the delay of a few tenths of a second to re-transmit the occasional dropped packet is seldom noticed.

But the demands of voice, video and so on are more rigorous. Hence the need for RSVP to reserve a sort of virtual channel through the Net to carry a steady stream of packets, in order.

As of 1997, RSVP was emerging from research labs into wider use. It was expected to offer the clearest benefits for MULTICAST services, which is what it was designed for. Some doubts remain about its ability to work for services like video-conferencing, which involve fewer recipients and a more equal two-way communication.

RTF
See RICH TEXT FORMAT.

RUN
To execute, for example, a computer program.

RUN-LENGTH ENCODING
A technique for DATA COMPRESSION, which works well on rasterised images and other data which are likely to contain long sequences of the same value. Instead of transmitting a run of, say, 1,000 0s – as might happen in transmitting the all-white background to a rasterised image – run-length encoding transmits an escape character (to denote that coded data follow), then the number of times that the value is repeated, then, finally, the value itself.

For repetitive data, this can shrink dramatically the quantities that need to be transmitted. But for data with little redundancy it can actually increase the quantities transmitted, because denoting one 0 requires more BYTEs than simply sending one 0. Run-length encoding is used in fax machines and many other applications.

SCANNER

A device which converts text and images into DI-GITAL form. Most scanners convert the continuous tones of a photograph or drawing into an array of dots, each of which stores the colour at a particular point on the original page. The number of dots that a scanner stores for each inch of page is called its optical resolution. Using SOFTWARE to interpolate new dots between those they have actually read, many scanners can create the illusion of finer resolution, and thus more detailed images, than they have actually seen.

SCRIPT

A kind of program. Typically a script is a program that co-ordinates the work of other programs. So, for example, a communications script might automate the dialling, LOG-ON and other exchanges necessary to connect with an ONLINE DATABASE. Because they customise existing programs, or automate small tasks, scripts are typically small and fairly simple.

SCSI

Short for Small Computer Systems Interface, a technical STANDARD which enables DISK drives and other peripherals to be connected to a PERSONAL COMPUTER.

SECAM

Abbreviation for Séquence Couleur A Mémoire, a STANDARD for colour television transmission developed in France and used there and in Russia, among other places. Like PAL it uses 625 lines of dots to make up a picture, but it codes the information that makes up the picture differently.

SEARCH ENGINE

SOFTWARE that finds things on the WORLD WIDE WEB. Type in a few of the words that the Web pages you are looking for will contain and others will not and – hey presto – back comes a list of material. Popular search engines include Altavista (*www.altavista.digital.com*), Excite (*www.excite.com*),

Hotbot (*www.hotbot.com*) and Infoseek (*www.infoseek.com*). Although more a catalogue than a search engine, YAHOO (*www.yahoo.com*) also runs searches.

The problem for all search engines is twofold. First, they must maintain up-to-date indices of the fast-changing INFORMATION on the Web, which they typically do by sending out a WEB CRAWLER to follow every link it can find, and catalogue the pages it comes across. The second, harder, problem is using those indices to provide information relevant to users' queries rather than an indigestible mass of data. Techniques for information retrieval are useful, but more work needs to be done to refine them. Search engines should provide the spur to invest in these refinements, for they are the busiest sites on the Internet and thus able to attract the lion's share of advertising revenue.

In the meantime, tips for effective searching include the following.

- If you know what kind of site you are looking for, try Yahoo, which has divided the universe of Web sites into categories ranging from CD stockists to nuclear physics references.
- If you just know the subject you are looking for, use a search engine.
- Be as specific as you can. Search engines do not understand grammar, but they do typically look for *all* the words you list. The more words you give them, the shorter the list they return.
- Be careful about phrases. Typing, say, *virtual reality modelling language* will return all pages that contain all four words, but not necessarily together. To search for the phrase, put it in quotes: "*virtual reality modelling language*".
- Use "not" to exclude extraneous material. In Altavista, for example, *privacy not electronic* excludes from the search Web pages which contain the word "electronic" and so concentrates on the real-world kind. (If you

poke around a little, you'll discover that most search engines allow a BOOLEAN EXPRESSION to create specific searches. See the help sections of the various search engines to find out how.)
- Keep trying. If the first try is too much or too little, adjust the search and try again. Doing is the only way to learn.

Relying on the government to protect your privacy is like asking a peeping tom to install your window blinds.
John Perry Barlow

SECURE ELECTRONIC TRANSACTIONS
See SET.

SECURITY
The process of protecting computers and their DATA from unauthorised access. The three main aspects of security are as follows.

- **Physical access.** Mainframes and other big computers are typically kept in a locked room to prevent prying or sabotage.
- **SOFTWARE access control.** Each user of a system may be granted, or denied, access to specific files. Passwords and other such mechanisms try to ensure that users really are who they tell the machine they are.
- **Encryption.** Coding data into illegibility can prevent even those who see it from understanding it.

The rapid growth of networks has caught security specialists in a triple bind. Physical access no longer matters much. It is possible to loot a computer in Atlanta from Amsterdam. Software access control schemes do not always work, sometimes because hackers are cleverer than systems designers, but more often because systems administrators are just plain careless. Yet the technology of encryption is only now becoming common and

---

convenient enough to use regularly, and the threat that new PUBLIC-KEY CRYPTOGRAPHY schemes might work all too well is causing governments to consider regulating their use. You just can't win.

SEEK TIME

The time required for a DISK to find a piece of DATA; on modern disks typically some thousandths of a second. Disks read and write data on to "cylinders", which run circularly around the surface of the disk, rather like tracks on a vinyl record (except that they do not spiral and they are not incised into the surface). One element of seek time is the time required for the read/write head to move to the proper distance from the centre of the disk; another element is the time then required for the spinning disk to rotate the relevant data to a position under the head.

SEGMENT

A division of MEMORY. Some early microprocessors, including notably those made by INTEL and used in the original IBM PERSONAL COMPUTER, assumed that no program would want to use more than some fixed amount of memory. In Intel's case this was 64 kilobytes, which with hindsight seems a ludicrously small amount. So it created a two-part scheme for finding code and DATA in memory: one part of the chip specified which segment the processor was then using, while a second specified where in the segment the data lay. This simplified the chip manufacturer's job at the expense of greatly complicating the programmer's, for when programs and data grew larger than 64k, as they quickly did, the complications of keeping track of the different segments were many and annoying.

SEMANTICS

Describes the correspondence between symbols and their meaning. In NERD usage, semantic errors denote the problems of a program which just does the wrong thing, as opposed to syntactic errors, which denote a program that does nothing at all because it has not been written in a form that a computer can understand. In English, "dogs have wings and fly" is a sentence containing semantic errors (because they don't and can't), while "walk dogs tail have and a" is a sentence with syntactic errors (because it is nonsense).

SEMICONDUCTOR

As the name suggests, a material which sometimes conducts electricity; that is, which is neither a conductor, like copper, nor an insulator, like asbestos. Silicon and germanium are good examples. What makes semiconductors so interesting is that, by adding small quantities of impurities called dopants, they can be made into devices which flip from conducting to non-conducting, and thus serve as switches for electrical current. Better still, they can do this very quickly, in a very small space and with no moving parts. Such "solid-state transistors", to use the jargon, form the basis of the silicon chip.

SERIAL

Describes DATA communications in which the BITs travel one after the other, in contrast to PARALLEL COMMUNICATIONS, which send a whole BYTE or word simultaneously.

SESSION LAYER

This part of the SEVEN LAYER REFERENCE MODEL controls synchronisation between interactive computers: which can send what sort of DATA when.

SET

Short for Secure Electronic Transactions, a PROTOCOL created by Visa, Mastercard and other finance companies to make electronic payments more secure. SET uses PUBLIC-KEY CRYPTOGRAPHY to ensure both the authenticity and the privacy of financial information.

SEVEN LAYER REFERENCE MODEL

A useful abstraction for classifying and organising technical standards for DATA communications, promulgated by the ISO. Each level, or layer, handles more and more detailed aspects of communication. By dividing the task into layers, communications technology can be broken up into components, each of which is shielded from changes, problems and complexity at other levels. The seven layers are as follows.

- **PHYSICAL LAYER.** Concerns the electromagnetic signals – electric pulses, radio waves, or light – which carry information across a channel.
- **DATA-LINK LAYER.** Concerns techniques for detecting and correcting errors, and for avoiding conflict when several computers want to access a communications channel at the same time. The data-link layer creates the illusion of a perfect, error-free transmission.
- **NETWORK LAYER.** Concerns the routing of packets from one machine to another across the NETWORK.
- **TRANSPORT LAYER.** Concerns the assembly and disassembly of messages – E-MAIL text, files or whatever – into the packets which are handled by the network layer, and those beneath it.
- **SESSION LAYER.** Adds facilities to the transport layer to handle more interactive applications. The session layer controls which computer can send which messages when, and other such synchronisation tasks.
- **PRESENTATION LAYER.** Concerns the COMPRESSION, encryption and coding of data.
- **APPLICATION LAYER.** Concerns the details of converting from the conventions used by one computer system to another; making sure, for example, that data are displayed correctly on the screen, or that FILE names conform to local naming conventions.

Because, say, the network layer can assume that the data-link layer will transmit its packets – and that it need not worry about how – this separation of responsibilities makes it much easier both to modify networks and to link different sorts of networks. Changes made at the physical layer need not concern any of the "higher" layers, nor need differences between different networks.

SGML

Standard generalised mark-up language, a programming language used to create formatted documents that can be easily transferred between one word processing, or text-formatting, system and another.

SHAREWARE

SOFTWARE that is freely distributed, so as many people as possible can try it out at no cost. Satisfied users are asked to pay a (usually small) fee to the author, and many do. One of the nice things about the ONLINE world is that it is still possible to make money by trusting in the goodness of your fellow human beings, at least so far.

SHOCKWAVE

A PROTOCOL and a PLUG-IN for a WEB BROWSER that allows animated films created with Macromedia's Director program to be played across the Web.

SIMD

Short for Single Instruction, Multiple Data, a way of organising the processors in a parallel computer. All of the processors work in lockstep, each executing the same instruction at the same time. (Contrast to MIMD, where different processors can execute different instructions.)

SIMM

Short for Single In-line Memory Module, a small PRINTED CIRCUIT BOARD on which are mounted eight or nine MEMORY chips, for ease of installation. Memory chips typically store megabits of DATA, yet computers naturally work in terms of megabytes. By installing eight chips at a time, BITs are turned to BYTEs and management is eased. (Nine chips adds an extra for computers which use PARITY to check the contents of memory.)

SIMMs are gradually being superseded by DIMMs, which allow more data to be written to memory in each tick of the processor's clock (64 bits instead of the SIMM's 32 bits).

SIMPLEX
Describes a communications channel which carries DATA in one direction only. (Contrast to DUPLEX.)

SIMPLEX ALGORITHM
A method for calculating optimal solutions to collections of equations. It is commonly used, for example, to minimise time wasted in servicing aircraft or, given a fixed shelf space and demand, to calculate what collection of goods are most likely to yield maximum profit. (See also LINEAR PROGRAMMING.)

SLIP
Serial Line Interface Protocol, a version of the INTERNET PROTOCOL adapted for the slow speeds and low reliability of dial-up telephone lines. Together with PPP, SLIP provides an alternative way of getting on to the Internet for those who cannot afford a LEASED LINE.

SMART CARD
A credit-card sized device which contains a MICRO-PROCESSOR and some MEMORY. Smart cards have two potential advantages over ordinary credit and ID cards. First, they can record the results of a series of transactions, so the card itself knows whether you have exceeded your spending limit, eliminating the need to call a central DATABASE to verify each transaction. In theory, smart cards could also contain a brief medical history, or any other DATA that a person might want to carry about.

A second potential advantage of smart cards is SECURITY. They can use their intelligence to employ quite sophisticated encryption schemes to protect data they carry, or to work with clever verification protocols to try to ensure that the person using the card is really its owner.

Despite these advantages, however, progress in

deploying smart cards has been slow. Part of the difficulty is simply the perennial chicken-and-egg conundrum of introducing new technology: smart cards are not of much use until there are lots of smart-card readers scattered about, and smart-card readers are not of much use until there are lots of people carrying smart cards. But another part of the problem has been the lack of a compelling application. With the growth of networks and electronic shopping, demand for electronic cash may begin to change all that.

SMDS

Short for Switched Multi-megabit Data Service, one of the first high-capacity DATA-carrying services offered to the public by telecoms companies. Strictly, the service offers 45m BITs per second of data-carrying capacity, but some carriers offer cheaper, lower-capacity services. In theory, SMDS lets the telephone company take over some of the hassle of managing long-distance links between LANs. In practice, the service is not widely used as most companies find leased lines cheaper and more convenient.

SMTP

Simple Mail Transfer Protocol, a set of technical standards for the transfer of E-MAIL from one machine to another. This is the mail PROTOCOL most commonly used on the INTERNET.

SNA

Short for Systems Network Architecture, a grand scheme by IBM to create an over-arching architecture that would incorporate all of the standards necessary to enable a wide variety of different computers and networks to work together. Like many grand schemes it has never been finished, having proved far more complex and difficult than its creators ever imagined.

SNMP

Simple Net Management Protocol, a technical PROTOCOL used to manage the operation of machines over a NETWORK: turning them on and off and otherwise making them do things. Perhaps the most famous use of SNMP is the INTERNET toaster. A toaster was connected to the Internet, and people from around the world were invited to control how brown its toast would be; just the sort of senseless technical trick that delights hackers. Despite some effort, the toast delivery problem was never solved.

SOFTWARE
Those information technologies that you cannot drop on your foot, particularly computer programs.

SOLID-STATE DEVICE
An electronic device whose workings depend on the properties of a solid chunk of matter, like the silicon in a silicon chip. This is in contrast to a vacuum tube, which worked by sending electrons across a vacuum. Because they involve no moving parts and a minimum of mechanical construction, solid-state devices are usually extremely reliable.

SOURCE CODE
The text of a computer program. What a human writes, as opposed to the OBJECT CODE, which is the sequence of 0s and 1s created by a COMPILER from the source code for a computer to read.

SPAGHETTI CODE
An unstructured computer program. In the early days of computing MEMORY was extremely scarce. As programmers struggled to cram more and more into fewer and fewer lines of code, the logical flow of their programs turned and twisted around itself so intricately as to resemble a bowl of spaghetti, hence the name. Needless to say, spaghetti code is hard to understand and hard to change without breaking. It is generally considered a bad thing.

SPAM
Unsolicited junk e-mail; mass-mailings which typ-

ically offer products you could never imagine
buying or opportunities to get rich quick (usually
by selling products you could never imagine anybody else buying either).

SPARC
A RISC chip used by SUN MICROSYSTEMS to build its
best-selling UNIX WORKSTATION.

SPECIFICATION
A detailed exposition of what a computer system
should do. A specification will typically include a
description of the business process that is to be
automated, the equipment that will be needed to
do the job, the screen interfaces through which
computers and people will communicate and a
step-by-step breakdown of the LOGIC that the program will follow.

In theory, good engineering practice dictates
that any significant system have a detailed and
accurate specification before writing code. But in
practice the ideal is seldom achievable. For one
thing, writing specifications is a time-consuming
process; the more time spent writing a specification, the greater the risk that the system will be
out of date by the time it is delivered. More prob-
lematically, to write a detailed specification for a
computer system which is meant to change dramatically the way in which work is performed,
perhaps as part of a RE-ENGINEERING effort, is to ask
people to imagine how work will best be performed in a world unimaginably different from the
one in which they now live.

In practice, specifications are often the IT
department's first line of bureaucratic defence in a
project that is going wrong. "That wasn't in the
specification" or "To do that we'd have to rewrite
the specification completely" are two phrases
often heard when new systems fail to live up to
expectations.

SPIRAL MODEL
An approach to building computer systems based
on steady, continual improvement rather than a

step-by-step progression to a fixed goal. (Contrast
with WATERFALL MODEL.)

SPOOLING

A technique to make more convenient communication between a computer and a PERIPHERAL
device. Spooling uses a BUFFER to store temporarily any DATA that the quicker machine might send
in advance of the slower one's ability to consume
it. That way the quicker machine need not be
always waiting for the slower one to catch up.

SPREADSHEET

One of the applications that made the PERSONAL
COMPUTER popular. Spreadsheets are an automated
version of the arrays of figures used by account-
ants to make financial calculations. Many rows or
columns in such spreadsheets are calculated from
previous rows or columns, according to fairly simple formulae. In the automated version, the user
enters the formula directly into the spreadsheet
and the computer keeps the calculations up to
date even if the numbers change.

The idea for the spreadsheet is said to have
come to Dan Bricklin – an entrepreneur who created VisiCalc, the first spreadsheet, for the APPLE II
computer – as he sat in a class at the Harvard
Business School, pondering a particularly tedious
blackboard-full of numbers. His idea sold millions
of computers. It is also said that spreadsheets
fuelled the takeover boom of the 1980s by making
it easy to perform the tedious calculations needed
to value a company under various assumptions of
its future earnings.

*It is ultimately unworthy for excellent men to lose
hours like slaves in the labour of calculation
which could safely be relegated to anyone else if
machines were used.*
G.W. Leibnitz, 1685

SQL
Structured Query Language, the programming lan-

guage most commonly used for asking questions of databases. It was originally developed by IBM. In theory, it offers a kind of *lingua franca* for databases; SQL can be used to access any DATA from any DATABASE that understands the language. Most databases nowadays speak SQL. Unfortunately, however, there are several competing dialects.

SRAM

Static Random Access Memory, a form of RAM. Like DRAM it stores the 0s and 1s of BINARY DATA as electric charges in the rows and columns of a grid of circuits. Unlike DRAM its circuits will hold their charge indefinitely; they do not need to be constantly refreshed. This makes SRAM faster and more reliable than DRAM, but also much more expensive.

STACK

A way of storing incoming and outgoing DATA in MEMORY which operates on a LIFO, or last-in, first-out, basis.

STANDARD

Like OPEN SYSTEM, another much abused phrase in computing. Strictly, a standard is a technical specification agreed by a national or international standard-setting body, like ANSI or the ISO. In computer-industry practice, however, standard-setting bodies often move too slowly to keep up with technology. So many widely accepted technologies become established as *de facto* standards. Instead of a single, detailed technical specification, like that created by a standards-setting body, *de facto* standards are typically created by copying the behaviour of the most popular version of the technology, or simply buying a copy of it. The hope of creating a *de facto* standard like MICROSOFT's DOS has in turn inspired marketers and advertisers to proclaim every new product a "standard". These days, it does not require too much cynicism to equate the phrase "emerging new standard" with "over-hyped, unproven, new product".

STANDARD GENERALISED MARK-UP LANGUAGE
See SGML.

START BIT
A BIT sent in many communications protocols to denote the start of a new character.

STATIC RANDOM ACCESS MEMORY
See SRAM.

STOP BIT
A BIT sent in many communications protocols to denote the end of a character.

STORE AND FORWARD
A simple way of constructing a computer NETWORK. Each computer has a rough map of the machines to which it is connected. When it receives a message it decides – guessing if necessary – which of the machines to which it is connected is closer to the message's destination. Then it stores the message until it has a connection to that machine, and sends it on. This technique was the basis of FIDONET, USENET and other early do-it-yourself networks.

STREAM
A general way of referring to the things inside a computer that generate or receive DATA. An input or output PORT can be a stream. But so can, say, the part of a program that generates a list of random numbers.

STRING
Techno-term for a piece of text, or any other string of characters in a row.

STRUCTURED PROGRAMMING
A 1970s panacea, which is still proving itself useful in the 1990s, even if it is not the answer to all an automator's woes. The idea behind structured programming is that computer programs, like machinery, should be composed of a collection of discrete components, each of which performs a

specific and well-defined function.

Use of structured programming was often accompanied by a complementary approach to problem solving, called top-down decomposition. The idea is to state the basic steps of a solution simply and at a fairly high level of abstraction. Then do the same for the steps of the steps, and so on, until a level of detail is reached that can be written as a computer program.

The basic component of a structured program is called a SUBROUTINE, and collections of related subroutines are often further differentiated by collecting them into modules. Modules are crucial for large programming projects. By dividing work into more or less independent chunks, they enable even large teams to work together without tripping over each other's feet.

The biggest difficulty with structured programming is that, unlike the promises made by some of its early promoters, it does not solve all of the problems of the known universe. Some problems do not lend themselves to neat top-down decomposition. While structured programming enabled programmers to create larger, more complex programs than they did before, really big programs still defeat it.

STRUCTURED QUERY LANGUAGE
See SQL.

STYLE SHEET
A way of specifying the layout of an electronic page: the fonts to be used, margins and so on. This is particularly useful for Web browsers because early versions of HTML allowed only rudimentary formatting specifications. There was no way, for example, to specify fonts or margins, and without control over these, page design could remain only very, very basic indeed.

SUBROUTINE
A basic component of a computer program; a small piece of code that does a specific job.

SUN MICROSYSTEMS

The leading manufacturer of UNIX workstations and, thus, also the supplier of much of the basic infrastructure for the INTERNET. Networking has traditionally been one of the strengths of Sun products. Sun's name was originally an acronym for Stanford University Networks and one of its founders, Bill Joy, worked with some of the creators of Unix from Bell Labs to build TCP/IP networking into the OPERATING SYSTEM. To power its systems, Sun developed the SPARC family of RISC microprocessors.

Although Unix workstations and file servers are Sun's core business, in 1997 it also began selling a NETWORK COMPUTER designed to run the Sun-developed JAVA language. These cheap, easy-to-maintain machines put Sun into direct competition with MICROSOFT and INTEL, owners of the technologies which now dominate the desktop.

SWAPPING

See VIRTUAL MEMORY.

SYMBOL-PROCESSING HYPOTHESIS

The idea underlying most approaches to ARTIFICIAL INTELLIGENCE, that intelligent activity can take place as the manipulation of symbols alone, without regard to their underlying meaning. A critical thought experiment to test the hypothesis is the "Chinese room" proposed by a philosopher, John Searle. The Chinese room works roughly as follows. In an isolated room lives a man equipped with a dictionary and a stock of tiles, each imprinted with a Chinese ideogram. Each entry in the dictionary relates one ideogram to another ideogram. In the morning the man is presented with a tray containing columns of ideograms. His task, over the course of the day, is to replace each ideogram with its corresponding entry from the dictionary. The man has no idea what any of the ideograms mean. The question is, is he "thinking"? Discuss this at your next dinner party.

SYNCHRONOUS

Having clocks ticking in unison, as opposed to ASYNCHRONOUS, where no attempt is made to keep clocks on the same time. When clocks tick in unison, there is no need to add extra machinery to communications protocols to synchronise two machines, like stop bits. But keeping clocks ticking in unison is typically more trouble than it is worth.

SYNTAX

Concerning grammatical structure, in contrast to SEMANTICS, which concerns meaning. Most errors in programs concern syntax: a missing comma here, or a mis-spelled variable name there. Fortunately, syntactic errors are usually easy for the COMPILER to detect and warn the programmer about. The really dangerous errors are where the program makes perfect sense, but not the sense that the programmer intended.

SYSTEMS ADMINISTRATION

The management of computer systems: includes setting up user accounts, running networks, repairing and recovering from errors, installing and configuring SOFTWARE, backing-up DATA and a host of other tasks, many of them thankless.

SYSTEMS ANALYSIS

The process of discovering and documenting how business processes work, and defining how computers can (it is hoped) make them work better.

T1 LINE

A standard US LEASED LINE, which offers 1.536m BITs per second of DATA-transmission capacity. The European equivalent is the slightly more capacious E1 LINE.

T3 LINE

A standard US LEASED LINE, which offers 45m BITs per second of DATA-carrying capacity. The European equivalent is an E3 LINE.

TAPE DRIVE

Tape cartridges are commonly used for back-up and archival storage of computer DATA. They can hold a lot of data (150 megabyte tapes are fairly common) and the technology is well understood and reasonably cheap. But tapes are also slow and vulnerable to snarling. As the technology matures, the tape drive is gradually being replaced by the OPTICAL DISK.

TCP/IP

The NETWORK protocols used on the INTERNET. It stands for TRANSMISSION CONTROL PROTOCOL and INTERNET PROTOCOL.

TDMA

Short for Time Division Multiple Access, another name for TIME DIVISION MULTIPLEXING.

TELEDESIC

A scheme backed by Bill Gates of MICROSOFT, cellular magnate Craig McCaw and Boeing to put several hundred satellites into low-earth orbit to create a seamless, high-BANDWIDTH DATA NETWORK accessible via radio links from anywhere on earth. The plan is to start service in 2002, providing up to 2m BITs per second of bandwidth on the uplink and up to 28m bits per second on the downlink, with a few very high-bandwidth channels of up to 1.5 billion bits per second for gateways and service providers.

TELEPRESENCE

The feeling of being there that people get from a well-crafted VIRTUAL REALITY program. More often used to describe the lack of feeling of being there given by most of today's virtual reality programs.

TELETYPE

The simplest form of TERMINAL, in which text, and only text, is sent to the screen character by character, line by line, with only the simplest of formatting. When a line fills, the next one is started. When a screen fills, it scrolls up one line. MICROSOFT's original DOS for the PERSONAL COMPUTER offered a teletype (TTY) INTERFACE, and Microsoft is now making billions selling WINDOWS SOFTWARE to make the machines easier and prettier to use. (Contrast with GRAPHICAL USER INTERFACE.)

TELNET

The process which enables someone to log-in to a remote computer and use its services via the INTERNET. Contrast to FTP, which enables a person to get DATA from a remote computer, or REMOTE PROCEDURE CALL, which enables a program to access the services of a remote computer.

TERA-

A terabyte is about 1 trillion BYTEs. Strictly, because computers count in powers of two rather than powers of ten, 1,099,511,627,766 bytes, or bits. (See also KILO-, MEGA- and GIGA-.)

TERMINAL

A screen and keyboard which enable a person to communicate with a computer. Also used loosely to refer to a PERSONAL COMPUTER when it is used largely to communicate with a MINICOMPUTER or MAINFRAME.

TERMINAL EMULATION

SOFTWARE which helps personal computers to communicate more effectively with large ones. In addition to managing communication, the software enables the smaller machines to understand the "magic" commands which position the CURSOR on the screen, or make characters stand out in bold.

TIFF

Tagged Image File Format, a technical STANDARD often used for storing graphics files on both UNIX machines and personal computers.

TIME DIVISION MULTIPLEXING

A way of allowing many different communications streams to share the same communications channel. Each is allocated its own series of time slots to keep it from becoming confused with the others. (See MULTIPLEX.)

TIME SHARING

The process of allowing many people and programs to use the same computer simultaneously. Each in turn gets a few milliseconds of time on the central processor to calculate. Because the switching is so fast, and takes clever advantage of the inevitable delays in input and output, it usually – but not always – appears that each has its own computer. (See also MULTI-TASKING.)

TLA

Three Letter Acronym, seemingly the technologist's favourite form of communication.

TOKEN RING

A popular way of managing the flow of DATA across a LOCAL AREA NETWORK. A simple discipline prevents computers from sending data at the same time and so garbling each other's messages. The computers continually pass a kind of electronic token from one to another, in order. Computers only send data when they hold the token. This is in contrast to ETHERNET, the other popular way of managing the flow of data across local area networks, which simply detects collisions between data, and requires the computers involved to send again (after each has waited for a random interval, to prevent the collision from happening a second time).

The extra overhead of passing the token means that token-ring networks are somewhat slower than Ethernet at light loads. But they can be less easily overwhelmed by heavy loads than Ethernet, and so are popular for factory AUTOMATION, and other applications where the volume of data traffic varies widely and assured performance is crucial.

TRANSISTOR

An electronic switch, which is turned on (conducting electricity) or off (not conducting electricity) by the application of a small electric current.

Moore's Law. The number of transistors that can be etched on to a given area of silicon doubles every 18 months.

TRANSMISSION CONTROL PROTOCOL

The TCP in TCP/IP, these technical standards determine how messages are broken up into packets for transmission over the INTERNET – using the INTERNET PROTOCOL – and reassembled again at the other end. In terms of the SEVEN LAYER REFERENCE MODEL, TCP corresponds to the TRANSPORT LAYER.

TRANSPORT LAYER

That part of the SEVEN LAYER REFERENCE MODEL which concerns standards for how communications – the text of an E-MAIL, say – should be assembled and disassembled for transmission over a PACKET NETWORK.

TROJAN HORSE

A program used to capture unsuspecting people's log-ons and passwords. Typically, a Trojan horse looks like the screen ordinarily presented when first logging on to a computer. But, unlike the usual screen, it records the LOG-ON and PASSWORD – where the creator of the Trojan horse can later retrieve them – before allowing the user to go about his or her business.

TRUSTED THIRD PARTY

Someone, or some company, who vouches that a given PUBLIC KEY really does correspond to the person who it purports to. The belief is that a trusted third party will oil the circuits of electronic commerce by giving people assurances that the "John Doe" who has electronically signed the purchase order they are about to ship goods against is really the "John Doe" who works in purchasing, and not some clever HACKER who managed to substitute his public key for Mr Doe's in an ONLINE directory. Cynics wonder if there are not easier ways to establish identity; after all, how many real-world transactions are co-signed by a notary public?

Controversially, the UK and other governments also propose that trusted third parties (TTPs) should be required to manage KEY ESCROW schemes; that is, holding copies of private keys corresponding to the public keys they hold, and passing them to security agencies when needed to eavesdrop on a communication. Leaving aside the morality of this idea, it seems to compromise the purpose of trusted third parties in establishing identity. The reason for certifying the identity corresponding to public keys is that the PRIVATE KEY corresponding to that public key is known only to a specific individual. That knowledge should be as unique as the script of a signature. By forcing individuals to compromise their control over the means by which their identity is established, governments would seem to be undermining the very surety they say they want to promote.

TTP
See TRUSTED THIRD PARTY above.

TTY
See TELETYPE.

TURING MACHINE
A simple, abstract model of a computer used in computing theory to show what a machine can and cannot do.

TURING TEST

A test of intelligence proposed by Alan Turing, a British mathematician and computer-science pioneer. A computer could be truly said to be intelligent, Turing proposed, on the day that it could hold a conversation with a person, and trick that person into thinking that it was one of them. Appearance need not matter; the conversation could occur by typing at a TERMINAL. But knowledge of language, common sense, reasoning ability and, probably, a sense of humour, would matter greatly.

Turing predicted computers would pass his test by the millennium. No chance. Hugh Loebner, a producer of lighted plastic disco dance-floors, has sponsored an annual Turing-test competition since 1991. A panel of judges converses with several terminals, each of which is connected to either a person or a machine. So far, telling one from the other has been as easy as telling night from day. Even if they try, few people can manage to be as monumentally stupid as a computer.

> *Not until a machine can write a sonnet or compose a concerto because of thoughts and emotions felt, and not by the chance fall of symbols, could we agree that machine equals brain.*
> Sir Geoffrey Robinson, 1949

TWAIN

Short for Tool Without an Interesting Name, a STANDARD for exchanging DATA between a SCANNER and the SOFTWARE that makes use of the scanned images.

TWISTED PAIR

The kind of wiring used in the telephone system; typically, as the name suggests, two copper wires twisted one around the other. Contrast to COAXIAL CABLE, which consists of a single, larger copper wire surrounded by shielding to prevent electromagnetic interference.

U

UART

Short for Universal Asynchronous Receiver/Transmitter, which usually refers to the chip that encodes and decodes DATA for transmission over the telephone line. In general, it denotes any chip that converts the parallel data STREAM within a computer into a SERIAL one, and vice versa.

UNIVERSAL RESOURCE LOCATOR

See URL.

UNIVERSAL SERIAL BUS

See USB.

UNIVERSAL SERVICE

In theory, a noble goal that motivates the world's telephone companies: to give everyone the ability to communicate. In practice, universal service is tied to a system of cross-subsidies that is coming into conflict with the two forces now driving the transformation of telecoms markets: technological change and market competition.

The creators of the first telephone networks had two problems in setting prices that everyone could afford. First, laying wires to remote rural locations cost more than wiring cities. Second, the cost structure of the telephone network, in which most costs were the fixed costs of NETWORK investment, translated awkwardly into pricing structures that homeowners and other small users could afford. Setting monthly or quarterly line rentals high enough to recover fixed costs would deter many homeowners from getting on to the network. Yet homeowners also did not talk on the telephone much, so they would not pay for themselves in per-minute charges either.

The telephone companies set up a system of cross-subsidies. As monopolies they could charge what they liked. So they charged high prices to business and long-distance users, and used the profits to cover losses on residential customers. Governments, in turn, codified the system of cross-subsidies in telecoms rate regulations.

Today that system, which worked comfortably

for half a century, is falling apart. New competitors are entering telecoms markets, and new technologies are creating new services. New questions bedevil telephone companies and their regulators. Who should pay extra for universal service? Which services should pay over the odds? Which should be subsidised? Not only are the questions hard to answer, but, worse, in doing so regulators second-guess the market. Instead of encouraging competition and innovation, they crush it by setting prices that favour one political constituency over another.

Finding new means to achieve the goal of universal service promises to be one of the biggest regulatory challenges for the remainder of the decade. In the USA, a charge was placed on second (and third and fourth...) telephone lines in order to help subsidise the cost of wiring schools and rural hospitals to the INTERNET. In the UK, some people are talking about trying to do away with cross-subsidies altogether. Whatever solutions are adopted will have a huge impact on the telecoms revolution, for better, for worse, or both.

In the first computer forecast of an election result, a UNIVAC computer predicted that Eisenhower would win by a wide margin in 1952. But broadcasters at CBS, whose election-night gimmick it was, did not believe the machine and fudged the results to be in line with conventional polls. The polls were wrong; the machine was right.

UNIX
Probably the most influential piece of SOFTWARE ever invented, Unix is a MULTI-TASKING OPERATING SYSTEM originally created at AT&T's Bell Laboratories in the early 1970s. At the time AT&T was the USA's regulated telephone monopoly, and so forbidden from competing in computer markets. It therefore freely distributed Unix, together with its source code, to universities. For two decades, computer-science students have had their impressions of what a computer should look like shaped

by Unix. At the same time they have used it as the foundation on which new innovations are built.

The INTERNET is built on Unix, via the networking facilities added to the operating system at the University of California at Berkeley in the late 1970s. The design of MICROSOFT'S DOS, the most popular operating system for personal computers, owes a large intellectual debt to Unix. The most popular programming language for small computers, C, was developed in conjunction with Unix. Unix's design philosophy – that computer programs should be small and designed to do a specific task well – has informed a generation of programmers, and created a host of small-but-useful tools for the programming community.

For most of its history, however, Unix's intellectual impact has overshadowed its use. It was adopted and extended by hackers, making it hard for ordinary mortals to use. The hackers themselves have fought bitterly over different versions of Unix, fragmenting the market. The two main camps have been AT&T's own version, called System V, and descendants of the version of Unix created at the University of California at Berkeley, called BSD (for Berkeley System Distribution).

Today, however, with the growth of networks, Unix is making inroads into the corporate world. SUN MICROSYSTEMS, the leading maker of the UNIX WORKSTATION, has tried to reconcile BSD and System V with yet another version of the operating system, called Solaris. Although it seems unlikely that Unix will start popping up on desktops, it may yet become the glue that holds corporate networks together, managing both databases and communications across companies and the world.

UNIX WORKSTATION

A high-powered desktop computer which runs the UNIX OPERATING SYSTEM. In the late 1980s Unix workstations were almost exclusively used for demanding computing tasks like COMPUTER AIDED DESIGN and scientific research. But as personal computers become more powerful – and equipped with lots of MEMORY and high-resolution screens

– high-end PCs increasingly compete for desktop tasks, while Unix workstations, in turn, are increasingly used to manage networks, as the FILE SERVER and in other back-room chores formerly done by a MINICOMPUTER.

UPLOAD
To send DATA "up" from a small computer to a larger one. (Contrast with DOWNLOAD.)

URL
Short for Universal Resource Locator, an address describing the location of a document, computer program or other resource used by the WORLD WIDE WEB. URLs are the Web's way of finding things. The strength of the Web is the way it unifies the different communications protocols used on the INTERNET, and the URL is where that unification occurs. The first half of the URL specifies the PROTOCOL which determines how communication is to take place: HTTP or FTP or mailto (to send E-MAIL) or whatever. The second half specifies what is to be communicated: the Web page or FILE to be downloaded or the e-mail address a message is to be sent to.

USAGE-BASED PRICING
Pricing schemes that charge by the amount of use made of the system. The telephone, for example, charges by minute or second of use; some DATA-transmission companies charge by the megabyte.

USB
Short for Universal Serial Bus, a communications technology that promises an end to the proliferation of sockets on PCs. USB is fast, sending DATA at up to 12m bits per second. It can connect up to 127 devices at the same time. Best of all, it promises to provide a single way of getting data into and out of a computer, replacing the collection of SERIAL ports, parallel ports and other I/O sockets.

USENET
The world's largest conversation, consisting of over 10,000 news groups, each using E-MAIL to dis-

cuss a specific topic, from *alt.sex*, unsurprisingly the most popular NEWS GROUP, to *comp.unix.wizards*, which provides technical advice on the more arcane features of the UNIX OPERATING SYSTEM.

The evolution of the USENET is an excellent example of why today's computer networks are different from yesterday's telephone ones. USENET was built from the bottom up. When Unix was first distributed to universities it had little technical documentation. To hackers interested in networks, however, this problem became an opportunity. To share technical information among hackers, they devised the UUCP communications PROTOCOL to enable far-flung hackers to talk to each other via their machines, using a STORE AND FORWARD approach. Thus USENET was born.

More recently, USENET has adopted INTERNET protocols to transmit messages. The two biggest issues facing USENET are over-popularity and censorship. Many news groups have become so popular that NOISE is beginning to drown out signal. At the same time, concerns over pornography have led some universities to ban the less socially redeeming news groups, like *alt.sex.bestiality*.

UUCP
Unix to Unix Copy Protocol, a way of moving files and E-MAIL from one UNIX machine to another. It is now largely superseded by SMTP and other INTERNET protocols.

UUENCODE/UUDECODE
These provide a way of sending programs and other BINARY files via E-MAIL. The problem they solve concerns the number of bits transmitted reliably. In binary files, all eight bits in each BYTE are crucial; in text files only the last seven really matter. In a short-sighted attempt to make them simple, some e-mail systems were designed so that they do not transmit the eighth BIT reliably. Uuencode and uudecode are used to translate binary files into a form which can be sent by e-mail, and back again. On the MACINTOSH, a program called BINHEX does the same thing.

V STANDARDS

A collection of technical standards set by the CCITT for modems.

Standard	Description
V.21	For DATA communications at 300 BITs per second. In the USA Bell 103A is more commonly used.
V.22	For data communications at 1,200 bits per second. In the USA Bell 212A is more common.
V.22 *bis*	For data communications at 2,400 bits per second.
V.32	For data communications at 4,800 or 9,600 bits per second.
V.32 *bis*	For data communications at 14,400 bits per second.
V.42	For error-checking and reducing line NOISE.
V.42 *bis*	For compressing data for faster transmission.
V.FAST	For data communications at 28,800 bits per second.

VALUE-ADDED NETWORK

A communications NETWORK which does more – and typically costs more – than the ordinary public switched network. More could mean higher BANDWIDTH, improved DATA-carrying capabilities, or just about anything an engineer can dream up.

VAPOURWARE

SOFTWARE that exists only in the marketing brochure. The software industry is notorious for announcing new products long in advance in the hope of deterring customers from buying a rival's product. Some long-promised products have never materialised.

VECTOR GRAPHICS

Refers to graphics in which the computer remembers the shapes by a description of their geometry – the line segments that make up the figures – rather than simply a BIT MAP of its representation on a particular screen.

VIDEO RAM
See VRAM.

VIRTUAL COMMUNITY
A group of people gathered electronically to discuss subjects of mutual interest. Virtual communities are one of the most heartwarming creations of new media, demonstrating that, when given the opportunity to come together, people can govern themselves both responsibly and creatively.

Virtual communities are typically highly specialised. They discuss plasma physics, parenting, pottery or pheasant-rearing, but only one at a time. They naturally evolve their own codes of conduct, and enforce them by exiling repeat offenders. They provide a wealth of experience and information on their chosen subjects, which is why companies are trying to create virtual communities to support their products by, say, sharing experience with managing SUN MICROSYSTEMS' workstations.

For all their strengths, virtual communities are different from real communities. They succeed by bringing out the best in people, allowing everyone to excel in a field of their own choice. There is no compulsion to join, and lots of other options for those who do not fit. Real communities, by contrast, must also keep the worst in people under control, ensuring that people who might not really like each other can still live side by side.

VIRTUAL MEMORY
A technique for enabling a computer to work as if it had more DRAM than is in fact installed. The trick is to swap the contents of a chunk of MEMORY on to the HARD DISK, and substitute for it something that will be needed sooner. The key, obviously, is to ensure that the stuff written to disk is not immediately read back in again (a research topic which has been the subject of many doctoral theses).

Often virtual memory is managed by organising memory into standard-sized chunks, called pages. The swapping of pages into and out of memory is, not surprisingly, called PAGING.

VIRTUAL PRIVATE NETWORK

A service offered by telephone service providers enabling big companies to tie together far-flung facilities into an apparently seamless network, which can be managed as easily and flexibly as if all the telephones were linked to the same PABX.

VIRTUAL REALITY

Imaginary worlds created by the use of high-powered computing technology. Virtual reality has been hyped as the ultimate extension of the human senses. It might, someday, enable people to work in worlds they could not otherwise experience; for example, to visualise the world inside a human vein, or to manipulate simulated molecules to help in developing more effective drugs. It might also enable people to create new worlds of the imagination. One pioneer of virtual reality research created an undersea world in which she lived and moved as a lobster (your fantasies may differ).

Today, however, the reality is more prosaic. The technology of virtual reality has three key components, each of which has much room for improvement.

- **Headsets.** In order to create the illusion of a three-dimensional world, virtual reality presents slightly different images to each eye using a head-covering pair of goggles. Today's are still heavy and clumsy.
- **Simulations.** To recreate an imaginary world, computers must be able to calculate how the world works: how bodies move and stretch; how much resistance to force they offer; how they break apart.
- **RENDERING.** In addition to calculating how the world works, virtual reality must make it look right. This requires the computer to create realistic-looking surfaces, textures and colours, which in turn requires brain boggling quantities of computing power.

In addition to getting the technology right, the elements must be combined in ways to convince the subtly sensitive human brain. A problem yet to be overcome with goggles, for example, is that goggle eyes in fact focus only a few inches in front of the face. This gives a feeling of claustrophobia instead of an illusion of depth.

VIRTUAL REALITY MODELLING LANGUAGE
See VRML.

VIRUS
A self-replicating and often malicious computer program. A virus typically stitches its code into that of another program. Each time that program is executed in a new machine, the virus looks for a way of infecting that computer as well.

Once it has infected a machine, the virus awaits some date or signal to work its mischief. Friday the 13th is a popular day for triggering viruses. So is Michelangelo's birthday. Once triggered, some viruses wreak havoc, say by deleting all files on a HARD DISK. Others merely annoy, by flashing messages on the screen.

To avoid infection by viruses, it is best to practice "safe computing". Avoid borrowing or sharing programs (especially with strangers), although DATA should usually be innocuous. Run an ANTI-VIRAL program frequently to try to detect infection before damage occurs.

VISION
Giving a computer vision is in one sense just a matter of hooking up a video camera. But getting it to see requires the machine to make sense of the images the camera presents. As in so many areas of ARTIFICIAL INTELLIGENCE, what seems trivially easy for people turns out to be desperately difficult for machines.

Part of the problem is that people bring knowledge to bear on the problem of visual understanding that machines utterly lack. When people view, say, a factory conveyor belt, they already know that it is likely to carry parts which are distinct from the belt, which move with it and which cast shadows. They use this knowledge to distinguish the parts of the scene. Machines, which lack this knowledge, just get confused.

Recently, however, researchers have begun having more success in computer vision by trying to train computers just to react to visual inputs, rather than to try to "understand" them. In the retina of a frog, for example, nerve cells are wired together so that they are highly stimulated by small, moving objects, like a fly. The cells react even before the frog has a chance to think about what he might be throwing his tongue at. By wiring up neural nets to mimic the instinctive reactions of nerve cells, researchers are teaching computers to recognise a variety of sights. One such, at Carnegie Mellon University, has been trained to recognise the road before a moving car, and it reacts in such a way that it does a pretty good job of driving.

VISUAL BASIC
The latest, most souped-up version of Bill Gates's old favourite, the BASIC programming language he dropped out of Harvard to create for the first PERSONAL COMPUTER, the MITS Altair. This one, however, has become the corporate choice for writing the quick and cheerful programs needed to make PCs really personal. It has two advantages over basic BASICs. First, the visual part: instead of writing code for WINDOWS and fancy user-INTERFACE boxes, the new BASIC lets the programmer work out with a MOUSE what the windows should look like and act like and then generates the code automatically. Second, Visual Basic is integrated with MICROSOFT'S WORD PROCESSOR, SPREADSHEET and applications SOFTWARE so programs written in Visual Basic can take advantage of these programs' capabilities. Many of the programs written in Visual Basic do little more than automate, link together and simplify work done by two or three applications programs. In the best traditions of engineering, it enables programmers to do as little as possible, borrowing instead the work of their predecessors.

VON NEUMANN BOTTLENECK
The motivation for parallel computing. Computers

derived from the basic conceptual designs laid down in the 1950s by John von Neumann, a scientist at Princeton University, have a fundamental limitation. They each have a CPU which executes instructions stored in main MEMORY, together with the DATA they work on. The faster the CPU works, the greater the percentage of its processing time it spends simply fetching instructions from memory. At some point, all of the increase in speed is consumed simply gathering instructions rather than doing the work which those instructions dictate.

One way to lessen the impact of the bottleneck is to use a CACHE. The idea is to try to anticipate which instructions will be needed next – which is often easy to do, for programs are often read sequentially – and move those instructions to an area of the central processor, called a cache, from which they can be quickly fed into the actual computing machinery. A theoretically better solution, however, is to have several processors working simultaneously, or PARALLEL PROCESSING.

VRAM
Video RAM, a type of computer MEMORY designed so that its contents can be simultaneously read (by a display screen) and written to (by the central processor). Most conventional forms of RAM cannot do both at once. Simultaneous access enables quicker, smoother graphics displays.

VRML
Short for Virtual Reality Modelling Language, a language for describing the three-dimensional scenes that make up virtual realities. By reducing 3-D scenes to a precise, compact description, virtual realities can be shared over the INTERNET.

VSAT
Very Small Aperture Terminal, a communications satellite whose transmissions cover only a small area of the earth beneath them. A smaller footprint means less risk of interference, and hence less need for regulation.

W3C

WORLD WIDE WEB Consortium, a group headed by
the Web's creator, Tim Berners-Lee, and situated
at the Massachusetts Institute of Technology. It
aims to guide the development of the Web, to create consensus over new technological standards
and to set the research agenda for new problems.
Its Web site, *www.w3c.org*, is the most authorita-
tive source for Web-related INFORMATION.

WAIS

Short for Wide Area Information Service, a set of
programs that tries to make available INFORMATION
widely scattered across the INTERNET. WAIS allows
people to search the world's documents for information on a given subject, and progressively
narrow the search to those relevant just to them.
Although the potential is vast, growth in the use of
WAIS has been slow, partly because it requires
time-consumingly prepared indexes to the DATA
before it can be accessed.

WAN

See WIDE AREA NETWORK.

WATERFALL MODEL

The traditional way of developing a computer system, in which each step, from design to testing,
follows one after the other. The problem with the
waterfall model, and the reason fewer and fewer
programs are being built this way, is the delays it
creates. Creating programs step by step can take
four or five years. Given the speed of change in
the business world, this can often make programs
irrelevant by the time they are completed.

WEB BROWSER

Software used to navigate the vast NETWORK of
hyperlinks that makes up the WORLD WIDE WEB.
Because browsers are the INTERFACE between the
user and the Web, and the Web is encompassing
more and more of the world's INFORMATION, competition to dominate the browser market is fierce.
Both NETSCAPE, the most popular browser, and

MICROSOFT'S Internet Explorer, are given away to most users in order to gain market share. At the same time their capabilities are being expanded by vigorous research and development.

The first prototype browser, created by HTML-inventor Tim Berners-Lee, could create and edit Web pages as well as read them. Its first-generation successors (such as Mosaic, created as a student project by Marc Andreessen, who later led development of Netscape's Navigator) could only read pages. The latest generation can also edit pages, manage E-MAIL, read USENET news groups, manage secure communications through encryption, run programs written in JAVA, manage PUSH MEDIA, share documents and generally help remote groups collaborate over the Net. As the Web becomes an all-encompassing interactive environment, the browser is becoming an all-purpose interactive tool.

The sheer popularity of the functions the browser provides, however, will eventually slow its growth. Many of the capabilities now provided by browsers are migrating into the OPERATING SYSTEM, notably the ability to understand Java and the ability to follow Web links. As this happens, browsers will increasingly compete on their ability to make vast quantities of information comprehensible – and so make it easier to decide which Web pages to read and why – rather than their ability to move DATA from one place to another.

WEB CRAWLER

A piece of SOFTWARE that follows the links that make up the WORLD WIDE WEB, usually in order to index all the pages it finds to make them available for a SEARCH ENGINE.

WEB MASTER

The person who manages a computer linked to the WORLD WIDE WEB.

WELL

Short for Whole Earth 'Lectronic Link. One of the first virtual communities, the Well was born of the mutual-self-help strand of California hippiedom that also created the Whole Earth Catalogue, a guide to tools and resources aimed in large part at would-be founders of communes. (Indeed, the Well was financed with the surprisingly high sales of the Whole Earth Catalogue.) It demonstrates the appeal and virtues of a VIRTUAL COMMUNITY.

WETWARE
The most traditional of computing technologies: the human brain. (Contrast with HARDWARE and SOFTWARE.)

WIDE AREA INFORMATION SERVICE
See WAIS.

WIDE AREA NETWORK
A NETWORK which links distant machines. Typically, at least part of a wide area network (WAN) traverses the PSTN; that is, it involves DATA carried by a telephone company.

WIDGET
A small component part of SOFTWARE that adds a specific piece of functionality to a larger system. The term probably originated with the X WINDOWS system, where widgets create new types of WINDOW that might, for example, be round rather than square or contain a small SPREADSHEET.

WINDOW
Generically, a window is a computer screen within a screen. It is a separate area that can show an entirely different view from other windows, which updates its text and/or graphics independently of other windows, and which can be adjusted in size independently of other windows.

WINDOWS
MICROSOFT'S latest step towards world domination. Windows is the OPERATING SYSTEM of choice for about 90% of the world's personal computers. It defines what they do, how they do it, what SOFTWARE they work with and what they look like.

W

Windows began as a way of prettifying DOS, by giving it a GUI like the APPLE MACINTOSH. The first two versions of the product languished on the shelf, but the third took off. Windows 3.1 became the fastest-selling piece of software ever. It made computers easier to use, but, unlike IBM's more-advanced alternative, OS/2, it did not require investment in more MEMORY or DISK SPACE.

Windows '95 was launched as the successor to Windows 3.1. Its chief claim to fame lay in its ability to protect programs from the sins of their colleagues. If one program crashed, it did not bring down the entire machine. Aimed squarely at the middle of the desktop, Windows '95 is flanked on both sides by other members of the product line. Windows NT is Microsoft's rival to UNIX. It offers fully pre-emptive MULTI-TASKING and the ability to cope with all the demands of busy networks. Windows CE, by contrast, is a scaled-down version of Windows designed for palmtop computers and other portable devices. Windows '98, the next generation of the operating system, is due in 1998. Eventually, Microsoft hopes to adapt the Windows interface to everything from television remote controls to supercomputers. Ambitious? Bill?

WIRE-FRAME MODEL
The skeleton which underlies most computer generated images and specifies the basic shape of the object. To complete the graphical illusion, RENDERING covers the wire-frame model with a realistic-looking surface.

WORD PROCESSOR
A program that edits text.

WORKFLOW
SOFTWARE designed to help manage the progress of work through an office. It typically helps to keep track of deadlines. It notes the order of the steps in which a task must be accomplished, and helps to ensure that work flows down its pre-ordained path. It can also help keep track of who must authorise a given piece of work.

Proponents of workflow point out that, by helping to prompt workers through complex tasks, it can ease the problems of coping with fast-paced, quick-changing office procedures. Critics, by contrast, argue that even simple office work has more subtleties than can be easily expressed to a computer. So the efficiency of workflow systems comes only at the expense of rigidity.

WORLD WIDE WEB

The technology that made the INTERNET usable by mere humans, the World Wide Web (WWW) is a system of HYPERMEDIA linking text, graphics, sound and video on computers spread across the globe. By making the Internet both a more expressive and easier to use medium, the Web should take most of the credit for that network's explosive growth.

The basic technology of the Web was originally created by Tim Berners-Lee at CERN, Europe's atom-smasher sited near Geneva, to help physicists keep track of all the DATA generated by their experiments. At the heart of the technology is a programming language, HTML, which allows a phrase or graphic in one document to be linked to another document anywhere on the global Internet. When a person clicks a MOUSE on that highlighted phrase, the linked document is fetched and brought to the screen automatically.

Refinements to the technology of the Web have expanded the use of links beyond simply fetching pre-existing documents. A LINK can also trigger a computer program which creates a document, say by querying a DATABASE. Or it can bring to the screen a form, to be filled in interactively. Or it can launch E-MAIL. In this way, the Web rapidly became an easy-to-use, general-purpose INTERFACE for the Internet and the computers on it.

By 1997 the Web had grown to encompass over 1m sites. They range from compendia of academic research to electronic shopping malls, from elementary schools to financial-services companies. One of the best features of the Web is its adaptability. It can distribute music as easily as financial data. Some of the more popular uses of the Web include the following.

- **Publishing.** Most print publications have a Web site to boost circulation. (See, for example, *www.economist.com* or *www.nyt.com*). Other publications exist only on the Web, like *www.slate.com* or *www.hotwired.com*, and so have the opportunity to adjust their editorial content to take advantage of the new opportunities of this new medium. Subscription revenue has been hard to come by for Web publishers; people have too many opportunities to get free information on the Web. But advertising revenue is growing fast.

- **Marketing.** A survey of American Web users by pollsters Nielsen found that half used the Web to research purchases. So it is not surprising that most big companies have Web sites to promote their goods and services. The majority have done little more than reprint electronic versions of their brochures and catalogues. The smart ones, though, have used the interactivity of the Web to enhance their brands. A classic example of this strategy is Federal Express. Its Web site, *www.fedex.com*, links to the FedEx logistics system so customers can type in their waybill number and find out exactly where their order is. This is a valuable service to customers. It also increases FedEx's reputation for reliability and saves a few million a year by eliminating many of the telephone enquiries about packages.

- **Electronic commerce.** In theory, selling from the Web has two key advantages over mail-order: there is no need to print and distribute catalogues or to maintain call centres full of people ready to pick up the telephone to take an order. In practice, the first companies to take advantage of these capabilities sold books and CDs, notably *www.amazon.com* and *www.cdnow.com.*

- **Research.** Most academic papers are now published ONLINE as discussion documents, from the lab or department Web site, long before they appear in formal journals. The journals will not go away, though, until there is some online equivalent of the peer-review process that paper articles go through for criticism and improvement before they hit the press.
- **Entertainment.** From quiz games to art galleries, the Web is filling with sights both edifying and unedifying and ready to fill a free hour or three.
- **VIRTUAL COMMUNITY.** The Web is host to a growing number of virtual communities, where people gather together electronically to discuss topics of mutual interest, from parenting to hi-fi.

Tim Berners-Lee still manages the development of the Web from his post at the head of W3C, a consortium dedicated to extending Web technology as needed to solve both technical problems, like providing better formatting of pages, and social ones, like providing ways to manage privacy and to limit children's ability to view pornography. Because of its versatility and the ease with which it can absorb new technologies, the Web is ideally placed to become the "meta-medium" which organises and unifies voice, video, data and other communications technologies as the technical process of convergence inevitably transforms the mixture of ANALOGUE signals which carry them into uniform DIGITAL packets. In the Web is the future of media.

Roughly 90% of those cruising the World Wide Web are male; most are in their 20s and 30s.

WORM
Write Once, Ready Many, a form of storage that writes DATA irreversibly to a DISK, typically an OPTI-

---

CAL DISK. It is useful for archival storage, but not much else.

WORM

A program that propagates itself across a NETWORK, automatically transferring itself to distant machines and running itself there (from whence it transfers itself to more machines). In contrast to a VIRUS, which secretes itself inside another program – and thus is only spread when the program carrying it is spread – worms take charge of their own reproduction. Perhaps the most famous worm was created by a computer science student called Robert Morris in 1988. In what seems to have been a misguided attempt to map the global INTERNET, Morris created a worm which replicated itself so rapidly that it brought thousands of computers to a standstill.

WWW

See WORLD WIDE WEB.

X.25

An international technical STANDARD for PACKET-SWITCHED DATA networks.

X.400

An international STANDARD for the transport of E-MAIL; an alternative to SMTP.

X.500

An international STANDARD for E-MAIL addresses, and directories. The goal of X.500 is to make it easy to find any e-mail address, easier even than getting a telephone number. Like many international standards, however, it grew unwieldy in the drafting, as each special interest added its little bit, and so is as yet little used.

X.509

An elaboration of the X.500 STANDARD designed to make it easy to look up the name associated with a PUBLIC KEY and vice versa.

XMODEM

A FILE-transfer PROTOCOL widely used on personal computers.

XON-XOFF

These two signals form a widely used way of controlling the flow of DATA across a communications line. When the receiving computer is getting more data than it can handle, it sends a xoff to the sender, which causes it to pause in transmission until a xon is sent.

XOR

Also called exclusive OR, this is an operation on two BITs which returns a 1 if and only if the bits are not equal (that is, if one bit is 1 and the other is 0). (Contrast to OR, which returns a 1 if the bits are not equal and also if they are both 1.)

X WINDOWS

The GUI most commonly used on UNIX. Developed at MIT, X, as it is commonly called, provides Unix

users with the conveniences of a MACINTOSH: resiz-
able windows on the screen to show different
views of DATA, a MOUSE to point and click with,
menus to choose commands from, and so on.

YAHOO

A guide to the WORLD WIDE WEB. Originally the part-time project of two Stanford graduate students, David Filo and Jerry Yang, Yahoo rapidly became the most popular roadmap to the fast-expanding World Wide Web, so the founders quit school and decided to make a business of it.

Yahoo (*www.yahoo.com*) differs from a SEARCH ENGINE in that it organises the Web by category. The approach is implied by the words behind the acronym: Yet Another Hierarchical, Officious Oracle. Yahoo enables searchers to work from category to subcategory, narrowing in on the sites they seek.

YMMV

Your Mileage May Vary, a phrase often used in E-MAIL to indicate that, well, your mileage may vary; that is, what works for me might not always work as well for you.

YMODEM

Yet another FILE-transfer PROTOCOL, commonly used on personal computers.

Z39.50

A technical STANDARD used to manage bibliographic information scattered across the networks. Z39.50 covers both the indices with which the DATA is organised, and the sort of queries that can be asked of it.

ZEROTH

A HACKER's term for first.

ZIP

A way of compressing files widely used on IBM-COMPATIBLE personal computers. Files so compressed are by convention denoted by the suffix .zip.

ZMODEM

Yet another FILE-transfer PROTOCOL for personal computers.

ZONE

A group of computers on a NETWORK. In a company each department might have its own zone, which is administered more or less independently from the rest. The obvious advantage of zones is that breaking up administrative problems into small pieces lessens their complexity, if only by making it harder for an administrator in one zone to inadvertently mess up another's computers.

Part 3
APPENDIXES

1 Abbreviations and acronyms

ACK	Acknowledgement
ADSL	Asynchronous Digital Subscriber Loop
AI	Artificial Intelligence
ASCII	American Standard Code for Information Interchange
ATM	Asynchronous Transfer Mode
BASIC	Beginner's All-purpose Symbolic Instruction Code
BIT	Binary Digit
CAD	Computer Aided Design
CALS	Computer Aided Logistics and Support
CAM	Computer Aided Manufacturing
CASE	Computer Aided Software Engineering
CCITT	French-language acronym for International Consultative Committee for Telephony and Telegraphy
CDF	Channel Definition Format
CDMA	Code Division Multiple Access
CD-ROM	Compact Disk, Read-Only Memory
CGI	Common Gateway Interface
CIM	Computer Integrated Manufacturing
CIO	Chief Information Officer
CISC	Complex Instruction Set Computing
CMOS	Complementary Metal Oxide Semiconductor
COBOL	Common Business Oriented Language
CORBA	Common Object Request Broker Architecture
CPU	Central Processing Unit
CRC	Cyclic Redundancy Check
CSCW	Computer Supported Co-operative Work
DBMS	Database Management System
DES	Data Encryption Standard
DIMM	Dual In-line Memory Module
DOS	Disk Operating System
DRAM	Dynamic Random Access Memory
DVD	Digital Versatile Disk
E-mail	Electronic Mail
EBCDIC	Enhanced Binary Coded Decimal Interchange Code
EDI	Electronic Data Interchange

EISA	Extended Industry Standard Architecture
EMACS	Editing Macros
EOF	End Of File
EPROM	Erasable, Programmable, Read-Only Memory
ERP	Enterprise Requirements Planning
FAQ	Frequently Asked Questions
FDDI	Fibre Distributed Data Interface
FIFO	First In, First Out
Fortran	Formula Translation
FTP	File Transfer Protocol
GIF	Graphics Information File
GIGO	Garbage In, Garbage Out
GNU	Gnu's Not Unix
GPS	Global Positioning System
GSM	Global System for Mobile
GUI	Graphical User Interface
HDML	Hyper Devices Mark-up Language
HTML	Hypertext Mark-up Language
HTTP	HyperText Transfer Protocol
IBM	International Business Machines
IETF	Internet Engineering Task Force
IO	Input-Output
IP	Internet Protocol
ISA	Industry Standard Architecture
ISDN	Integrated Services Digital Network
ISO	International Standards Organisation
ISP	Internet Service Provider
JANET	Joint Academic Network
JCL	Job Control Language
JPEG	Joint Picture Experts Group
K	Kilo
LAN	Local Area Network
LDAP	Lightweight Directory Access Protocol
LED	Light Emitting Diode
LIFO	Last In, Last Out
LISP	List Processing
M	Mega
MAE	Metropolitan Area Ethernet
MIDI	Musical Instrument Digital Interface
MIMD	Multiple Instructions, Multiple Data
MIME	Multipurpose Internet Mailing Extensions

MIPS	Millions of Instructions Per Second
Modem	Modulator-Demodulator
MOO	MUD, Object Oriented
MPEG	Moving Pictures Experts Group
MRP	Materials Requirements Planning
MUD	Multi-User Dungeon
NACK	Negative Acknowledgement
NC	Network Computer
NNTP	Net News Transfer Protocol
NTSC	National Television Standards Committee
OLAP	Online Analytic Processing
OLE	Object Linking and Embedding
OLTP	Online Transaction Processing
OPS	Open Profiling Standard
PABX	Private Automatic Branch Exchange
PAL	Phase Alteration by Line
PC	Personal Computer
PCI	Peripheral Components Interface
PCMCIA	Personal Computer Memory Card International Association
PDA	Personal Digital Assistant
PGP	Pretty Good Privacy
PICS	Platform for Internet Content Selection
Pixel	Picture Element
POP	Post Office Protocol
POTS	Plain Old Telephone Service
PPP	Point to Point Protocol
PROM	Programmable, Read-Only Memory
PSTN	Public Switched Telephone Network
PTT	Post, Telephone and Telegraph
RAID	Redundant Array of Inexpensive Disks
RAM	Random Access Memory
RFC	Request For Comments
RISC	Reduced Instruction Set Computing
ROM	Read-Only Memory
RSACi	Recreation Software Advisory Council
RSVP	ReSerVation Protocol
RTF	Rich Text Format
SCSI	Small Computer Systems Interface
SECAM	Séquence Couleur A Mémoire
SET	Secure Electronic Transactions
SGML	Standard Generalised Mark-up Language

SIMD	Single Instruction, Multiple Data
SIMM	Single In-line Memory Module
SLIP	Serial Line Interface Protocol
SMDS	Switched Multi-megabit Data Service
SMTP	Simple Mail Transfer Protocol
SNA	Systems Network Architecture
SNMP	Simple Net Management Protocol
SQL	Structured Query Language
SRAM	Static Random Access Memory
TCP/IP	Transfer Control Protocol/Internet Protocol
TDMA	Time Division Multiple Access
TIFF	Tagged Image File Format
TLA	Three Letter Acronym
TTP	Trusted Third Party
TTY	Teletype
TWAIN	Tool Without an Interesting Name
UART	Universal Asynchronous Receiver/Transmitter
URL	Universal Resource Locator
USB	Universal Serial Bus
UUCP	Unix to Unix Copy Protocol
VRAM	Video Random Access Memory
VRML	Virtual Reality Modelling Language
VSAT	Very Small Aperture Satellite
WAIS	Wide Area Information Service
WAN	Wide Area Network
WELL	Whole Earth 'Lectronic Link
WORM	Write Once, Read Many
WWW	World Wide Web
YMMV	Your Mileage May Vary

2 World's largest IT suppliers, 1996

Rank	Company	IT revenue, $ bn
1	IBM	75.9
2	Hewlett Packard	31.4
3	Fujitsu	29.7
4	Compaq	18.1
5	Hitachi	15.2
6	NEC	15.1
7	Electronic Data Systems	14.4
8	Toshiba	14.1
9	Digital Equipment	13.6
10	Microsoft	9.4

Source: Datamation.

3 Worldwide PC shipments

Year	Units, '000
1980	609
1981	1,631
1982	4,893
1983	11,123
1984	15,044
1985	14,705
1986	15,064
1987	16,676
1988	18,061
1989	21,327
1990	23,738
1991	27,265
1992	32,407
1993	38,843
1994	47,900
1995	60,171
1996	70,861

Source: Dataquest.

4 DRAM prices

Year	\$/megabyte
1974	24,576.00
1975	11,264.00
1976	8,521.73
1977	4,804.99
1978	3,467.58
1979	3,167.21
1980	2,136.62
1981	844.58
1982	599.97
1983	521.95
1984	381.82
1985	89.39
1986	81.26
1987	90.67
1988	125.84
1989	78.70
1990	47.84
1991	32.52
1992	23.44
1993	27.49
1994	26.15
1995	15.38
1996	4.29

Source: Dataquest.

5 Computers connected to the Internet

Date	No.
Aug 1981	213
May 1982	235
Aug 1983	562
Oct 1984	1,024
Oct 1985	1,961
Feb 1986	2,308
Nov 1986	5,089
Dec 1987	28,174
Jul 1988	33,000
Oct 1988	56,000
Jan 1989	80,000
Jul 1989	130,000
Oct 1989	159,000
Oct 1990	313,000
Jan 1991	376,000
Jul 1991	535,000
Oct 1991	617,000
Jan 1992	727,000
Apr 1992	890,000
Jul 1992	992,000
Oct 1992	1,136,000
Jan 1993	1,313,000
Apr 1993	1,486,000
Jul 1993	1,776,000
Oct 1993	2,056,000
Dec 1993	2,217,000
Jul 1994	3,212,000
Oct 1994	3,864,000
Jan 1995	4,852,000
Apr 1995	5,706,114
Jan 1996	9,472,224
Jul 1996	12,880,699
Jan 1997	16,146,000

Source: Internet Society.

7 Recommended reading

Champy, James and Hammer, Michael, *Re-engineering the Corporation*, HarperCollins, New York, 1993.
Over-optimistic, perhaps, but still the re-engineering Bible.

Forester, Tom (ed.), *Computers in the Human Context*, MIT Press, Cambridge, MA, 1991.
An interesting, if ageing, collection of essays on the social, business and human impact of information technology.

Freiberger, Paul and Swaine, Michael, *Fire in the Valley*, Osborne/McGraw Hill, Berkeley, CA, 1984.
Out of print, but still an excellent history of the invention of the personal computer.

Kelly, Kevin, *Out of Control: The Rise of Neo-Biological Civilization*, Addison-Wesley, Reading, MA, 1994.
An amazing collection of neat stuff, mostly to do with new technology and its impact on life as we know it.

Krol, Ed, *The Whole Internet User's Guide & Catalog*, O'Reilly & Associates, Sebastopol, CA, 2nd edition 1994.
First and probably still the best of the user's guides to the Internet.

Levy, Stephen, *Artificial Life*, Jonathan Cape, London, 1992.
A good, non-technical introduction to the field.

Pool, Ithiel de Sola, *Technologies of Freedom*, Harvard University Press, Cambridge, MA, 1984.
Still the classic work on the regulation and politics of new media.

Raymond, Eric, *The New Hacker's Dictionary*, MIT Press, Cambridge, MA, 3rd edition 1996.
How to decode a coder, plus some jokes.